Past Lives
- Future Voices

2010 Poetry Competition for 11-18 year-olds

Essex & Kent

Allison Jones

First published in Great Britain in 2010 by

 Young**Writers**

Remus House
Coltsfoot Drive
Peterborough
PE2 9JX
Telephone: 01733 890066
Website: www.youngwriters.co.uk

Foreword

Young Writers was established in order to promote creativity and a love of reading and writing in children and young adults. We believe that by offering them a chance to see their own work in print, their confidence will grow and they will be encouraged to become the poets of tomorrow.

Our latest competition 'Past Poets - Future Voices' was specifically designed as a showcase for secondary school pupils, giving them a platform with which to express their ideas, aspirations and passions. In order to expand their skills, entrants were encouraged to use different forms, styles and techniques.

Selecting the poems for publication was a difficult yet rewarding task and we are proud to present the resulting anthology. We hope you agree that this collection is an excellent insight into the voices of the future.

Contents

Colchester High School, Colchester

Dartford Grammar School for Girls, Dartford

Friends' School (Study Centre), Saffron Walden

Gravesend Grammar School for Girls, Gravesend

Hayes School, Hayes

Helena Romanes School, Great Dunmow

Holmesdale Technology College, Snodland

The Poems

Sorry

'Sorry I didn't do my homework, Miss,
really it wasn't my fault.
My little brother ate it you see,
once he ate two bags of salt.'

'Sorry I didn't do my chore, Mum,
but I am not the one to blame.
A virus deleted my memory, you see,
I can't even remember my name.'

'Sorry I was late coming home, Dad,
but a man gave me a Chinese burn.'
'What's that got to do with being late?'
'Nothing. I just thought you might have concern.'

'Sorry I forgot to take my medicine, Dr,
I was at the cinema with my friend.
Did you see how much popcorn he bought?
He really knows how to spend.'

'Sorry I didn't do the research, Mr Smithet,
I have forgotten the same type of thing before.
A virus deleted my memory, you see,
just like I forgot to do my chore.'

'Sorry I tried to skip school, parents,
but have you seen the lessons they make us do?
Mrs Stallsley is the worst, by far,
once she confiscated a boy's shoe!'

'Sorry I didn't use your bike in the race, Dad,
but that rusty thing was falling apart!
If I used your bike in the race,
it would have fallen apart from the start.'

Mark Pickett (12)
Bower Park School, Romford

1

He Pops Home
(Inspired by 'She Pops Home' by Cal Clothier)

He pops home just long enough
To overload the washing machine
To leave dirty socks on the kitchen floor
To be the first one to use Dad's aftershave
To play football in the garden and knock all Mum's flowers down
He pops home just long enough
To eat the spaghetti supposed to be for dinner
To kiss a tenner out of Mum
To sit on the sofa and make all the pillows creased
To make a stain on the new cream carpet
He pops home just long enough
To break a new crystal glass that is one of Mum's favourites
To rip a page from the local newspaper of a fit girl
And hang it up for everyone to see
To steal the car keys off the side
He pops home long enough
To crash out on the sofa and watch the footie
To throw a party when Mum and Dad are on a business trip
To make Mum feel bad so she will drop him into town
He pops home just long enough
To horrify his parents with some of the things he's done
And to leave them puzzled and dreading till next time
He pops home just long enough
To light his parents' day up like twinkling stars in the midnight sky
He pops home just long enough.

Amber Gurnett (13)
Chase High School, Westcliff-on-Sea

2

He Pops Home
(Inspired by 'She Pops Home' by Cal Clothier)

He pops home just long enough
To leave his clothes on the floor
To use the hair gel and leave it all over the sink
To beg a tenner out of Mum
To kick the football in the house
To play the Xbox 360 all day
He pops home just long enough
To raid his sister's piggy bank
To bring ironing home for Mum to do
To blare music out too loudly
To tell us about his love life
He pops home just long enough
To use all of Dad's new deodorant
To not clean up after he has cooked
To leave the toilet in a mess
He pops home just long enough
To horrify them that he's got a girl pregnant
To leave them praying till the next time
He pops home just long enough
To bring their garden back to life
He pops home just long enough.

Jazmin Brook (14)
Chase High School, Westcliff-on-Sea

3

He Pops Home
(Inspired by 'She Pops Home' by Cal Clothier)

He pops home just long enough
To leave his clothes lying all over the floor
To spend a couple of hours on the PS3
To leave urine all over the toilet seat
To eat the leftovers for supper
To not wash himself properly
He pops home just long enough
To use the last of the toilet roll
To kick the football around in the garden and wreck it
To take the tenner out of Mum's wallet
To play his music loudly enough to make his parents angry
He pops home just long enough
To bring mud into the kitchen
To leave the TV on all night
To mess up the mirror with gel
He pops home just long enough
To horrify them with the taking of drugs and drink
To leave them shaking till next time
He pops home just long enough
To illuminate them with excitement and love for another day
He pops home just long enough.

Thabo Tuso (14)
Chase High School, Westcliff-on-Sea

4

He Pops Home
(Inspired by 'She Pops Home' by Cal Clothier)

He pops home just long enough
To leave clothes on the floor
To bring mud into the kitchen
To eat all the food
To turn the music up too loudly
To leave food on the floor
He pops home just long enough
To take money from his sister
To spend too much on expensive clothes
To leave a bite in the last roll
To leave gel on the mirror
He pops home just long enough
To leave the TV on
To raid his dad's drawer for pants
To leave plates on the floor
He pops home just long enough
To horrify them with smoking and drinking
To leave them crying till next time
He pops home just long enough
To light up their eyes like the shining sun
He pops home just long enough.

Aaron Halliday (13)
Chase High School, Westcliff-on-Sea

He Pops Home
(Inspired by 'She Pops Home' by Cal Clothier)

He pops home just long enough
To have a fight with Mum and Dad
To swear at his sister
To hit his little brother
Make a mess of his room
He pops home just long enough
To kick a ball around the house
To forget to ring his friend
To steal money off the table
He pops home just long enough
To go through his sister's drawers
To flood the washing machine
To cover the mirror with hairspray
He pops home just long enough.

Sarah Baker (13)
Chase High School, Westcliff-on-Sea

Life Is Cruel

Witches are plotting wicked plans,
Their victims waiting in the unknown.
All is happy and untouched,
But little do they know,
Life is 'bout to turn bloody.

Death will meet them while 'tis dark,
Back-stabbed by ones who were allies.
Trust none with the fruits of your life,
As it will be you who regrets forever
And ever in the eternal afterlife.

There are two sides to this life,
Both lead to death, one way or another.
Stay noble and you die in cold blood,
Stay evil and die of old age with the burden
Of having killed your friends.

Kawarpal Chahal (14)
Chigwell School, Chigwell

6

The Shadow

Darkness engulfs the great hill of Roke,
Amongst the grass the wind screams and chokes,
The silence screams in the quiet before the storm,
But this unlucky tale, no oracle could've forewarned.

Such a young boy, yet such a big head,
Overconfidently attempting to summon the dead,
Yelled three times the name 'Elfarran'.
But something else escaped from Death's land.

A black splodge of ink on a golden globe,
The cold air around it even seems to erode,
A hideous monstrosity without head or face,
Yet without a name, in any language or faith.

Four deadly talons, like razors, but black,
Leap high in the air for an offensive attack,
Silently glide down, a swift black art,
Whilst sucking the very life-force out of your heart.

The young, jealous wizard, swept high off his feet,
As his power and his wisdom begin to deplete,
All students flee, except one loyal friend,
But strong paralysis causes his bravery to end.

All hope seemed lost, but then shone a light,
The only thing that darkness cannot fight,
The beast backs away confused and afraid,
From the still body where the wizard is laid.

The Archmage appeared out of the dark,
And drove the beast back with mighty a spark,
Then, with white staff of elm,
Brought the child back from Death's realm.

And although the battered wizard's alive,
The thing he let loose also survived,
That day on Roke Knoll he will never forget,
His terrible ordeal is not over yet . . .

Kyle Dewar-McKay (12)
Chigwell School, Chigwell

7

Skeletons

I

In short,
I was in love with a skeleton.
We'd lie, face-to-face, only a turf carpet between us,
And death.
A mere universe to travel.

II

Night is not dark, simply misunderstood.
It does not tell, simply watches as I
Descend to lie beside him.
At one with our mother as she tunnels my fingernails.
Earth lies ravished.
Willing prisoner to a wooden fortress where time
Just
Stops.
Reunited we lie.
Dry-eyed; no more I cry.

III

Slander saturated the tabloids.
They didn't understand.
Broken windows, graffitied walls,
And a bleeding, mutilated doormat punctured with hate.

IV

I no longer see darkness
Only bright gleaming white.
Walls and walls of white.
Bony, enamel white.

Now we both lie alone,
Him in light.
Me in darkness.
Skeletons.

Rachel Bradley (18)
Chigwell School, Chigwell

8

English Monologue

It all seems old and faded away,
yet those glorious days of triumph,
those adventurous days, on my way across the seas,
shall forever remain as my life's treasure; and are perhaps the
only reasons why this old man still wishes to keep life's breath,
even though he nearly has reached the brink of death.
As life's sun sets and the night approaches,
my skin, just like the old leaves, begins to wrinkle,
leaving behind this decay of my outer shell;
the arms which were once tough and as strong as steel,
capable of any might, and to give those Black Sails flight,
now have withered and their power seems lost.
Long back, those muscular arms, which none could give a match,
now have become too weak, too brittle, too rigid and stiff to support.
Just like the twigs of the trees, the bones crack.
The eagle's eyes that never failed to spot any bandit fleet, which
could even see several miles through the fog, all day and night,
today, are left with little remaining sight, and are blurred
by bleak blackness.
The glimmer of those beautiful whiskers now has disappeared,
for no more is it the age of gold, but the age of silver.
The spring of life seems to have long gone by.
The autumn has already arrived,
and still there's winter the barren tree must go through.
Now this old man has nothing to do and must lie on the bed,
for it is just before long he shall join the dead.

But a traveller cannot restrain from travel,
though now withered I am, I must say I have lived up to life.
The gamble of life which I began with
now does seem worth it.
Many have sailed through life's silent sea, but only few
through the stormy sea.

Abhijit Jha (15)
Chigwell School, Chigwell

9

Emptiness

Grey rooms
A grey view
The divide against emotion
but
the assault continues.
Each drop
against the window of my mind
is a constant reminder of my pain
hammering at my sanity.
With each strike
the window cracks
till the pressure overwhelms.
Emotion
floods through
washes out my room
and drags me out
Kicking
Screaming.

Under the light of emotion
your true self is revealed
stripped of shadows and façades
so you crawl
back to your room
and work
on blocking out the emotions
the feeling
the truth.
But one emotion
is locked in
forever, a penance
for your folly
the bitter taste of melancholy.

Stuart Innes (15)
Chigwell School, Chigwell

The Abbey

The bells chime twelve
She runs from the abbey.
Her footsteps echo
About the courtyard . . .

She crept through stones and mud,
To the looming abbey,
As it looked down
On its unkempt garden.

Eerily, for the hour, it breathed fire
From its mighty windows,
Whilst sinister chants,
Rose up from its walls.

Moonlight poured into the place,
As the door invited her in.
Light was thrust across her.
The chanting stopped.

Hollow eyes gazed through
Skeletal faces. Cloaked bodies
Glided towards her
Trembling figure.

The chanting grew
To feverish pitch.
The clothed corpses
Gathered around her.

The bells chimed twelve,
She ran from the abbey.
Her footsteps echoed,
About the courtyard.

Esther Barratt (17)
Chigwell School, Chigwell

I'm A Diary

I lay there on her desk, like a mother,
Waiting for her child at the school gates.
Soon they will be reunited.
Apart from her, I only have one good friend
And his name is Pen.
I am like her pet, for am forever loved, forever looked after.
I am her friend yet I am a weapon
That can be used against her.
She looks to me for salvation
And although we have never spoken,
And we are not even related,
I know her better than anyone else.
I cannot breathe, yet I live my own life.
Every day is an adventure, every day of the year.
I can change my mind, one day I'm happy,
The next I am sad.
My face is clean and decorated in flowers,
And although I have no eyes,
I know how she feels.
I can't offer her comfort,
I can't reach out and hug her.
On lonely nights, her soft hands hold me to her heart.
That's where I belong, but maybe her heart lives in me.
All I feel are her hands and her tears on my pages
Like the gentle pitter-patter of rain onto the forest floor.
When she cries, her memories are washed away from my pages
Like a river breaking its banks.
When all my pages are full, I am forgotten,
Yet I do not die, living the same life,
Over, and over, and over again.

Freddie Cooper-Rendu (13)
Chigwell School, Chigwell

12

Dark

Dark is that dingy room
Where dirty hands did their work.
Dark are the dank recesses
Of my demon-riddled mind.
Dark, which was once light,
Guiding me along the way.
A light, showing me right from wrong,
Correcting me when astray.
But now only dark.
Never ceasing.
For that is my life,
My fate and forever after.
Dark.
How sadistically funny,
That something you really want,
Will only cost your moral self.
That's what I thought at the time,
A small price to pay
So that I may reign.
But now it won't stop raining,
Outside or in.
The perpetual darkness, the rain, the cold,
All a sign.
A reminder of that past night,
A reminder of my sin.
For with this dark night,
I may never see the truth again.
Dark.

Richard Stavri (14)
Chigwell School, Chigwell

13

The Teddy Bear

I lie around all day; not knowing, not thinking.
But my chestnut coat is mangled and unloving.
Small puffy clouds float around silent within me,
While pools of sorrow, deep and black, linger woefully.
The gathering time is shown and behold,
My thinning hairs unfold . . .
The trueness of our life.
And so with a button she swivels
And two chubby stumps,
I hold her close and show the magic of our love,
I shine a glowing smile since birth to life . . .
My throne, the highest of all;
Looking down on my subjects and killing their pride,
I hold myself and feel the power.
But . . .
I fall, this time she won't pick me up,
A new home for dust mites,
I am unrecognisable.
They snigger, my reign is over now.
With solemn hours to happy celebration, but fife!
My home, a small, bleak hole in my pattern.
She has gone, and the magic is removed.
I dream of happiness, my love forever.
Shipped off to an unknown land.
My mistress's secrets unknown to all,
Hidden deep within the depths of my unbeating heart;
Surrounded by protection, white with innocence.
Memories lost from another world.

Sarah Chamberlain (13)
Chigwell School, Chigwell

14

Dictionary

I am a useful tool, accurate and precise,
An ocean of words, dry but overflowing with knowledge.

I know the words of every poet, play and book
Yet I do not speak, forever muted.

I am used to translate and understand,
Written in every language, have many additions
And come in all sizes.
Yet I remain incomplete and will forever be rewritten.
As time goes by I become older and wiser.

I am hardly read, often gathering dust, yet I remain a must.
I envy my cherished neighbours,
But I am the one that the reader favours.

I am the key of my world but I fear my throne.
One day I'll be thrown into the web.

I perch on the top shelf,
Where my owners do not search.
I have a clear view of the room that I am kept in,
I observe the tiny rays of light gradually creeping into the room,
And see the last glimpses disappear into the night.

The room is like an isolated island,
Where the objects within are left cold and alone, abandoned.
Left to be corroded by the darkness.
Everything sits in silence, waiting for something to stir.

I am trapped between my neighbours like a prisoner behind bars.
The thesaurus, atlas and encyclopaedia are my friends
And sufferers of the same fate.
Day after day watching in hope to be opened,
Waiting to release my expertise.

Haider Imtiaz (13)
Chigwell School, Chigwell

15

The Direction Of Time

Resonance in paradise,
The everlasting movement goes on,
Round and round,
For day and night,
Recording wrong and right.

Lasting an eternity,
Yet shorter than a single second,
A snail's pace,
A cheetah's race,
Staring you in the face.

There's never pause for thinking,
No, no stop, no rest, no end, no start,
Like liquid
Flowing, growing,
Seeping, slowly blowing.

Absolute and infinite,
Exploding in majestic power,
Igniting,
Enflaming the
Walls of reality.

Will the cycle ever cease?
Or will the wheels keep turning throughout?
We know its name,
Identity,
Time is calling out to me.

William Lord (12)
Chigwell School, Chigwell

16

Secret Diary

I'm full with secrets, memories and dreams,
My spine is strong to protect all of this.
I have trust enclosed within me,
Although it's sometimes ripped out.
I am a friend to tell all secrets to,
Like a brother, sister, mother or friend.
I am a safe haven without a doubt,
But I'm hidden away during the day
And only needed in times of excitement, inspiration or despair.
I am a good listener but I have no choice,
The same faces and stories every day,
Like a broken record continually playing.
Their tears are cried on me and I absorb their smiles,
Every memoir is etched into my skin
Like a permanent tattoo.
To them, being in my presence is always worth the while.
In me their lives will always remain,
I am a reminder of the highs and lows.
But soon I am no use,
With no space for any more tales.
At first I was blank,
Like a canvas with no picture.
But now I'm full to the brim with thoughts, hopes and ideas
That are impossible to erase.
So now I am forgotten,
Abandoned by the ones who once loved me and confided in me.

Robyn Schaffer (13)
Chigwell School, Chigwell

17

The Mad Destroyer

It lurks around looking for its lunch-time prey

Three eerie eyes patrol glancing every single way

Those hairy legs what a horrendous horrible sight

With sores and scars and bleeding scabs yet to heal

A horn fixed high and mighty on its head

Armed with tortuous teeth which tear and rip into any foe

Claws that scratch and cut and catch
Standing upright and still it rises all of seven feet

This beast it lives and breathes for battle

The fight, the feel the accomplishment of never failing

Its hunt for food above substance, heals and helps its mind

A monster of dread this mad destroyer full of might

Scares all living life during the terrible light of day.

Annabel O'Reilly (12)
Chigwell School, Chigwell

A Creed For Youth - Cinquain

'I'll grow,'
she said with hope,
no longer on tiptoes.
Will I stand, and tell their lies from
the truth?

Megan Coates (16)
Chigwell School, Chigwell

18

Patchwork Hearts

Sitting on the rooftops, staring at the stars,
A hundred glistening souls, hanging in the dark,
Strung to the velvet tapestry of gods,
Shining out the beauty of the long forgotten past.

A life without love fades to dark,
Mere thimbles of light from futile sparks.

Spinning through puddles, as the stars begin to swim,
And tiny trembling mirrors, fall on polished skin,
Weaving their silver rhythm through the sky,
Drumming out sorrows to a sympathetic night.

A life without love turns to dust,
Mere fragmented lyrics of broken trust.

Marble shoulders wear a midnight shade of pain,
With glowing highlights, as the moon begins to wane,
Tracing fragile threads that speak life's story,
A dream-catcher of scars, torn by reality.

A life without love falls as ashes,
Mere shivering splinters of shattered wishes.

Amidst the endless song of light and shadows,
Two pairs of nimble feet dance mirrored sorrows,
Soft spiralling steps in a collision of worlds,
Patchwork hearts to each other unfurl.

Amelia Hunt (17)
Chigwell School, Chigwell

Anne Boleyn

I lie,
A swollen mother. I burst,
Barren. Life's syrup stains the sheets.
There he is: evidence.
The pillow's corner cuts
My neck, slicing. I can feel the blood.

Pippa McKenzie (16)
Chigwell School, Chigwell

19

The Plug

I am plastic and sleek,
Black and silver,
Used everywhere, by everyone,
The head of conductivity, lacking mortality,
I want to be happy
But no, you say,
I am so fed up
Just throw me away.
My best friend is the wire
Constantly loose like a cannon
Attached to me like a lace
Only if it had a face
The things it would say
The things it would do
Only if it was like you.
You are many, we are few
I feed off power, eating by the hour,
Nothing's taking place if I am replaced,
3 or 2, I am flexible
Very accurate power to the decibel
Leave me hanging on the wire
Take me for granted, I'll set a fire,
The worst is to come, be prepared,
When I arrive nothing shall be spared!

Param Sura (13)
Chigwell School, Chigwell

Sleep

Take a look at that face staring into the void.
What do you see?
Is it pale and ailing,
One that has had too many troubles?
Is it weak and indifferent,
One that cannot fight the Devil anymore?
Is it lifeless, still and dead,
One that has no blood running in its veins?
Is it tired of pretence and patience,
One that has taken its mask off after the masquerade?

Take a look into its watery eyes.
Are they green, blue or brown?
One cannot distinguish anymore.
Can one see through them, see into the soul behind them?
Is it great, kind and noble,
One that has been betrayed and hurt?
Is it dark, evil, and feels not,
One that has no morals and emotions anymore?

Take a look at that face staring into the void.
It rests in peace,
Finally found what it's been looking for . . .
Eternal sleep in the stone-cold bed of the land of unknown.

Stanislava Georgieva (18)
Chigwell School, Chigwell

The Traumatised Creature

The traumatised creature dangles through the trees
With its tail, topsy-turvy through the trees
As it shreds the trunk, with its sharp razor-like teeth
It crunches and munches on the leaves with its elusive tongue
The prickly spikes protect it in long drawn battles
Sometimes it makes you shake and shiver until you fill with fright.
Skin silvery grey, hair hanging lank
Beware the monster brew, its grim and gristly stew.

Daniel Whitehead (12)
Chigwell School, Chigwell

Gothic Poem

Wafer-thin paper promises,
Born of social fetters,
These empty letters drip with façades, we fail to see
how wrong this is,
Cling to a charade, creepers around convention,
Without it we'd fall, so we clamber and crawl, climb and claw,
Pot-bellied with pop culture, gorged with carrion,
we carry on greedy like vultures.
To parry every stab of consciousness,
snatch and grab to go on like this is.
Any glitch in the system, any nugget of wisdom,
any clatter of a cloven hoof met aloof tangled words to hide the truth.
Every fairy story has a sting in the tale, every myth turned gory,
bliss is the story as the abyss is yawning.
Every song sung, reverberates a knell rung, we sing louder over the
ringing, deafening ourselves to death. And each breath gets shorter
and caught, lands like mortar fire at the door.
The taps of Thanatos, the blows of a hammer across our shoulders,
we battle upstream like salmon to escape the onset of coldness.
Corruption sifts down like snowflakes, turning squat hideous
buildings
into temporary wedding cakes. Gilding the ugly truth with a pure face.

John Stannnard (17)
Chigwell School, Chigwell

Clouds

Clouds are different in shape and size,
If they're full of snow it's like winning first prize!
Clouds bring sadness, clouds bring joy,
When they're full of snow that's what I enjoy!
Clouds can be angry and black,
So that's when I turn my back!
But then again a cloudless day,
Makes me so happy, to be out and play!

William Weightman (11)
Chigwell School, Chigwell

Imprisoned

I sit on a bed
Cold, hard, lonely, waiting
Waiting for the sound
It will come
It always does.

My heart jumps
Someone speaks
It's not for me
Five minutes yet.

I miss that smell
The smell I know,
Disinfectant and plastic
Is not the same.

'New boy, new boy'
My heart sinks
As tears begin to flow,
It cannot go on!
Mum,
Goodbye,
Sorry.

Alex Hartland (16)
Chigwell School, Chigwell

The End Of The World

Children stopped playing.
Dogs stopped barking.
People stopped moaning.

Suddenly . . .

People started moaning.
Children started playing.
Dogs started barking

And the whole world . . .

Isabella Sawtell (12)
Chigwell School, Chigwell

23

Outside The Classroom

I sit in the classroom
But outside it is raining.
The teacher spews information towards the students,
Which passes straight over their heads
Like the rain clouds outside that drift carefree
Over my school.
The pen sits in my hand.
But I do not write.
Words form in my mind, but they drift away
From my focus before my hand has a chance to write them.

The barrage of questions at the teacher
Drums in my head like the drumming of the rain
On the rooftop.

The rock of my chair falls in rhythm with the footsteps
Of a shielded passer-by. She is shielded by the flimsy umbrella
That attempts to defend the woman from the power of the wind.

My gaze follows this struggling adventurer until my attention
Snaps back to the teacher who demands an immediate answer
To his question, for which I have no
Answer.

Lewis Justin Jackson Clegg (16)
Chigwell School, Chigwell

The Sea Serpent

The serpent silently snaked through the seaweed,
The killer devastatingly destroyed all in front of it,
Its colossal-sized jaws clamped around the helpless shark,
The beast burrowed its head into the seabed,
The predator's venom polluted the water,
The serpent dominated the dark sea waters,
It surged through the sea waters silently,
It followed the eight-legged octopus,
The deadly beast dominated the water.

Jevan Rana (12)
Chigwell School, Chigwell

24

Raising The Shadow

Words of mystery fill the sky,
A black clot of darkness unfolding.
Duller than the deadliest evil,
Like the corner of your bedroom at night.
A shadow is brewing . . .

Obscurity and mist,
Beastly moaning and groaning.
Hot wind whining,
Grass tossing and twisting.
The shadow is coming . . .

'Elfarran . . . Elfarran . . . Elfarran!' he cried.
Finally, the beast unleashed its power,
Attacking with rage his compelling master.
Falling flat on the floor, life sucked out of his body.
The shadow is here . . .

Then suddenly the darkness faded,
And the stillness was restored.
The light and dark in balance again,
Moonbeams shone back over the hill.
The shadow was gone . . .

Thomas Turner (13)
Chigwell School, Chigwell

The Bone-Breaking Beastly Beast

It's the Deadly Destructor
In the salty sea
Its beastly breath
The sailors scream
Still the Deadly Destructor
Crushed corpses
The gigantic, growling beast
It's a hungry hunter
A devious demon

it lives in the deep depths
it stalks its scared prey
it bundles through the creaking boat
no survivors, they are all shredded
goes down to the dark depths
are crashed onto the coastline
it keeps gaining strength
with a haunting howl
down in the darkness.

Thomas Martin (11)
Chigwell School, Chigwell

25

Snow Leopard - Haikus

Clothed in fresh grey storm,
Eyes full of sagacity,
Grace and power flow.

Her own monarchy,
Surrounded, a white pasture,
Before her trembles.

Silent, focused gaze,
Huntress becomes the hunted,
Unseen, rifle poised.

A single bullet,
Her reign is overpowered,
Why this punishment?

A miniscule cell,
Sweltering, ball of fire,
Juries' own pleasure.

Eyes devoid of life,
Great blocks of ice, grey foam falls,
Home so far away.

Alice Palfreman (13)
Chigwell School, Chigwell

The Dangler In The Dark!

A leaf falls then light disappears,
Darkness awaits within death,
He dangles day and night,
Creeping slowly catastrophe is there,
He has no soul he makes me shiver,
His bloodshot eyes are eagerly looking,
He stares me down till I can't survive,
I didn't want to go but I'm already gone,
He's the dangler in the dark,
Peacefully waiting for his next prey to come . . .

Amirah Iman Chaudhary (11)
Chigwell School, Chigwell

26

War

Lives are lost,
buildings destroyed.
All for the cost
of Man wanting more

Teens are enlisted,
to 'fight for their country'.
Not that they wished it
but Man wanted more

Mothers are grieving,
for husbands and sons
While more men are leaving
so Man can get more.

The innocent slaughtered,
man, woman and child.
Struck down by mortars
because Man still wanted more.

So I ask you,
do you want to hear more?

Nathan Scott Edwards (12)
Chigwell School, Chigwell

My Monster Poem

The traumatised creature dangled from the creeping branches,
His razor teeth gnawing at the tree trunk,
His prickly spine proves to be protective,
His enormous height takes him to the heavens,
His intelligent mind makes him a mastermind,
His pongy breath is like a swarm of bins,
His sniping eyes sense luminously in the night sky,
His locked claws stick to the evergreen tree,
His elf-like ears sense his enemy for he has no predators,

His dangerous ways make you densely fear him.

Henry Tang (12)
Chigwell School, Chigwell

27

Grapes

Grapes are tasty,
Grapes are nice,
Grapes are all I eat at night,
Grapes are green,
Grapes are red,
I like to eat grapes in my bed.
If you like grapes, raise your hand,
Then you can join in my band!
Grapes are used in wine,
Grapes are oval,
I like to crush grapes with my feet.
Greeks used grapes to feed their wives,
Grapes can be smelly,
I like to eat grapes with ice cream and jelly!
Grapes are fragile,
Healthy too,
They have lots of iron just for you!
Grapes are one of your five-a-day,
Never throw a grape away!

Femi Fanibi & David Sullivan (12)
Chigwell School, Chigwell

Haikus

Stands tall in the hot
Mediterranean sun.
Seeing everything.

Swaying in the breeze
Shading the ground from the heat
Of the sun above.

When people see me
They stop and stare for a while,
Steal my coconuts.

Rickesh Bedia (14)
Chigwell School, Chigwell

Macbeth's Poem

The terrible witches, the demons of horror
Witches of deception, not witches of honour
Creators of spells, a revolting illusion
Leaving strong men with a feeling of confusion
The sound of their breath is as loud as the wind
Persuading innocent men to admit they have sinned

I feel I'm going mad, I'm going insane
I can only hope the guards get the blame
Poor Duncan, for he thinks all is well
Little does he know I will see him in Hell
I can sense the power rippling through the knife
The fact I'm about to take another man's life.

My heart is pounding, no time to think
I see the blood trickle like thick red ink
My ears are deafened, my eyes are blinded
I can't move my limbs, it's as if I were binded
The only one that's awake, the only one that's in life
Are my shaking fingers gripping the knife.

Cameron McKenzie (13)
Chigwell School, Chigwell

In Death's Image

Blood of innocence seeps from Death's wound
Spouting terror into the incandescent dark
Dark revelries enchant the light
Removing it from the wanted path
As ghosts and spirits wander among us freely still
The souls of men fear what is to come
The flames of virtue are extinguished
In the dark fog that hides black raven watchers
Cries and breath can be heard from afar
But none behold what is within our hearts
As Death summons a sleepless cry for all to hear
His servants awaken and spread despair.

Lauren Drabwell (13)
Chigwell School, Chigwell

29

The Storm

A storm is brewing in the sky,
It's getting worse, it just won't die.
The rumbling of thunder, the pitter-patter of rain,
The sound is making me go insane.

Slowly the clouds draw in on me,
It's killing me, can't you see?
The strength of the storm is increasing by day,
The night draws in and fades away.

Lightning strikes again and again,
No wonder it's sent me down the death lane.
The storm is spreading at a fast speed,
I don't know why but I've done no bad deed.

Soon the storm becomes very weak,
But still all the days are looking so bleak.
Finally now the storm has died,
The skies are free, there's nothing to hide.

Neha Patel (11)
Chigwell School, Chigwell

Untitled

On the bleak battlefield, men fought bravely.
The rebels were defeated, their will to fight destroyed.
The great hero was justly rewarded, he almost jumped for joy.
At the hill in the mist, he was told about his future, his evil deeds.
His future would be great but terrible, to go through with it,
He wasn't sure.

He would have power, but not happiness.
To get his power, he would have to kill his master and friend.
His dear wife greedily agreed to the idea,
And eventually changed his mind.
At the night of the murderous deed, both were dreadfully frightened.
So they wouldn't be suspected, they would shift the blame.
Now the hero was given his power, but lost his happiness.

Sam Smith (14)
Chigwell School, Chigwell

It's A Secret . . .

I may not mean anything to you
you don't even realise that I'm here
but I mean everything to her
and I can't just disappear.

I am easily influenced
by others, easily changed
ruin lives in a second
yet I am physically nothing.

You can't even see me
no matter how hard you look
but you can feel me
feel my presence around you.

Everyone wants to know me
but hardly anyone will.
Do you wonder who I am?
Well . . . it's a secret.

Natasha Gandhi (15)
Chigwell School, Chigwell

A Riddle Of Importance

I support you in times of trouble,
I am sturdy when you are week,
I may have no emotion,
Yet my importance is dismissed.

I could be snazzy and flash,
I could be bland and boring,
I could be expensive,
But I could be cheap.

Adults use me as a substitute when they are tired,
Grannies see me as a rival,
But children love me,
And that's all that matters.

Taylor Bedworth (14)
Chigwell School, Chigwell

31

Gruesome

A gruesome battle resulting in a gratefully received victory,
The windswept wasteland holding the witches heralding the future,
Hallucinated or genuine prophecies, perplexing more than one,
A brave combatant returns crowned with grandeur and credentials,
The focal message delivered by a hasty horseman,
The spouse's thoughts of sovereignty leading to severe conclusions,
Meticulous masterminding completed surreptitiously,
Her persuasive character cause deep dismay,
A future king facing thoughts of astounding assassinations,
Delirious, fantastical images of a hovering dagger encrusted
with blood,
A shrieking owl ominously signalling the accomplishment
of the murder,
Blood-coated hands refusing their owner of redemption,
One in torment, one proud but gradually turning insane,
A persistent knocking, the murderers are pursued,
One knows the facts; he was once a friend, now a foe.

Katie Marshall (14)
Chigwell School, Chigwell

Macbeth Poem

The soil of Scotland is stunned,
Witches' wicked ways leave people wondering,
Bold blood overflowing,
Moonlight murder shines ever so brightly.

Greediness has shown gruesome colours,
Friends forever finished out of fear,
Crying calls vanish into the mist,
Mission nearly missed, for there's one left to murder.

Beautiful blue seas cannot clean red,
The raging red fights and stains blue,
Guilt cannot guide them now,
For wealth and power wheels those to be misled.

Humza Nijabat (14)
Chigwell School, Chigwell

32

The Catcher

The Catcher slowly crept	from his crypt
Searching for his prey	prodding throughout the night
Hunting for a meal	no meat to be found
What should he do?	As he wanders around
He hears a sound	he gets up and looks around
But it's only the wind	whistling through the night
He's been tricked	but he's trying again
Watching over there	is something worth snatching
Fighting for its life	forgetting all its lighting
He's the Catcher	catching is what he does
He lives	a never-ending life
No hint of age	hiding away
Family he has not	for he is lonely forever
Sadly, silently	sobbing all day
His heart aches	asking for his love to stay
He is strong and mighty	never showing his fear
I feel pity	for this poor creature here.

Noor Sara Shah (12)
Chigwell School, Chigwell

Bloody Hands

From the door I hear a thud,
My hands, they are covered in blood.
I'm standing here full of guilt,
It's too late now, my nerves have built.

Outside an owl, loudly is sounding,
The pressure's too much, my heart is pounding.
I'm trying to be calm, alone with my wife,
I have to do something, I'm holding the knife.

I have to find, a way to flee,
When I do, I'll be filled with glee.
I can feel it; they're coming for us,
I have to go quickly, without a fuss.

Felix Rosen (13)
Chigwell School, Chigwell

33

The Angel

I have been sent to watch over you by your sister.
To look after and care for you for all eternity.
Whether you are near the place you once called home,
Or are off to a far and distant land,
She will be in your heart, for your every need.
A smile to take you places or a shoulder to cry on
In your time of need.
I am the angel that lies around your wrist,
Your blood flows past me as it does in her heart,
And the water washes over me, changing nothing.
Here I am linked to you by a thread of silver and nothing more,
But there she is linked to your heart by more than words can
describe
An unbreakable,
Sisterly bond.

Amanda Bacon (15)
Chigwell School, Chigwell

Dagon The Sky Lord

The monster's name, Dagon
His gigantic body
The red glittering scales
The beast beating at the ground
Riding the air majestically
Blood on his talons
His tail swatting the air

Dagon's fiery breath hot
He flew to his cave
The beast arose waiting for
The monster sprinted into the river
He buzzed into the sky
The grand behemoth flew
Dagon was the sultan of

death to all he sees
growling under the Earth
gleaming in the moon.
big paws smashing the land
swooping down on mankind.
dripping down below
throwing ghastly smells
around.
scorching insignificant houses
and fell to the ground, dormant
another fiery day.
slurping up water,
ready to get breakfast
and bellowed his defiance
the sky, the savage titan.

Shamus Anwar (12)
Chigwell School, Chigwell

34

The Wait

I'm waiting on the bridge in the darkness.
The silent rain embraces me in its misty shroud
leaving jewels settled in strands of hair
for which I no longer care, nor wipe away.
The evening offers little comfort as cold stars
shine dimly above me.
I'm still waiting, waiting, for
A familiar face?
No, it's only my shadow - its outline illumined
by the lamplight.
The only other figure in this wilderness.
A sudden movement - could it be . . . ?
Alas, it's gone - I'll never know.
The night draws in.
I'm waiting . . .

Ali Beagley (16)
Chigwell School, Chigwell

The Ant

I, the red ant, crawl through the reeds of the carpet.
Huge grey trees sticking up from the ground below.
My pointy, sharp tail pricking the lady's ankle like a needle.
Moving my way through the large crowd,
I suddenly get stepped on, but I'll stay strong.
I don't wail, I move along, pricking the nearest human to me.
I'm immortal, just can't be beaten, can't be killed, even shoes
won't crush me.
I won't die,
Time to prick that old man with the walking stick.
Still can't be beaten, still all alive.
Oh no! Not a foot!
A large, smelly foot stepping on my little body,
I meet my faith, up in Ant Heaven,
At least there are more people to prick up there.

Laurence Brooks (12)
Chigwell School, Chigwell

35

Why?

Oh squiggly line in my eye,
I see you there lurking on the periphery of my vision,
But when I try to look at you, you scurry away . . .
Are you shy, squiggly line?
Why only when I ignore you, do you return to the centre of my eye?
Oh squiggly line, it's alright, you are forgiven.

Oh clicking of my fingers,
I hear you creeping out of my grasp,
But when I try to grab you, you slip away . . .
Why are you so inconsistent, clicking of my fingers?
Why only when I forget about you, do you slide back?
Oh clicking of my fingers, leaving is forbidden.

Oh woman of my dreams,
Why do you do this to me?

Sasha Rosshandler & Sagenth Kugathasan (15)
Chigwell School, Chigwell

A Family's Blood

The Dark Hand lingers within the Black Nothing,
Allow your Wispy Weapons to tighten firm.
Thou has taken with maleficent yearning.
My hungering heart wishes to return
The disgraceful, soul-splintering, punctured hole.
For my mind swoons and staggers with vengeance.
The haze of rage renders my being out of control,
The eternal listening hears my utterance
'Let her fall, the wasted one, let it be done.'

'Twas this being that bore this torn, tarnished child.
I was the serpent suckling at her breast!
And like a serpent, I will curl around her chest.
Free my father's honour from the barren mother
Clytemnestra shall drop, dripping her royal blood.

Cameron Randall (17)
Chigwell School, Chigwell

36

Time To Go

And with that you were gone,
It felt like waking from a dream,
You were gone in a cloud of tears
And confusion,
Just wishing I could say goodbye
Or see you again.

Drifting in and out of sleep,
I knew it was time to go,
Another year, another week, another day,
Was all I needed
To say goodbye,
But I knew, it could not be,
Nothing more, nothing less,
It was time to go.

Kirsty Spencer (14)
Chigwell School, Chigwell

My Glasses' Case

I am opaque and talkative
Open my lid and you can hear the sound of chatter
My hinges are like a one-toothed mouth
I have the sound of a chatterbox.

My insides are as smooth as a baby's face
Feed me with transparent windows you can see through
And I will lock inside the gift of sight.

My outside is a turtle's shell
I am light and portable
I teleport from place to place.

I can be left in your car
Yet I'm patient enough to wait
But don't forget to take me to the cinema.

Guy Colman (13)
Chigwell School, Chigwell

37

Success Or Pretender?

I hang around the necks of men;
Strangling at their lives,
Gripping on their hopes.
I am a symbol of order
In a place of chaos.
When I'm round your shoulder,
You may be admired,
You may be loathed,
But I give you something,
Something to hide behind
Whilst cowering in your fleshy corpse,
Uninspiring, unfeeling,
Success or pretender
Weak without me.

William Cooper-Rendu (15)
Chigwell School, Chigwell

Prophecy

The aspect of prophecy lingering in the atmosphere,
Amid the sound of drums to war,
And as the victorious return, bloody from a battle of brutality,
A prophecy awaits them in close proximity on the putrid heath.
And two silhouettes gallop gallantly upon their noble steeds,
Them too, victorious against the volatile acts performed
On that very day.
And as they hurtled through the dank heath,
They sought shelter.
However, danger has not ignored these two courageous soldiers,
Near was a form of witchcraft brewing up divination,
And suddenly they meet and a prophecy is told,
And whatever may be told here is all well,
But what is done with it summons them to Heaven or Hell.

Alex Bromwich (13)
Chigwell School, Chigwell

38

The Betrayer

Bleeding and bloody, back from battle,
Malicious murder made by Man,
Powerful prophecy put him in the line,
Dying Duncan in his dorm,
Forceful lady, fearless like fire,
High upon the heath, he first met,
Wild voices of witchcraft,
Interesting idea in his mind,
Dangerous dagger he can see,
Scared soul sacrificed,
Unexplained unusual circumstances,
Drugged bodies die in sleep,
Smeared with blood of a selfless man,
Betrayer of his best friend.

Erika Osborn (13)
Chigwell School, Chigwell

A Murderer's Movement

To gain, but with guilt.
For him no vengeance, just victory.
But still his heart hurts.
He lingers no longer,
The bedroom beyond him,
The knife in his hand,
And his mind made up.
Safe and secure,
For no one will know,
Except him and his love.
A hole in the heart,
Is soon to be seen.
But the murderer's movement
Channels him back to his chamber.

Joshua Banfield (14)
Chigwell School, Chigwell

Unpleasant Prophecies

Queens and kings are being killed,
Unpleasant prophecies are being fulfilled.
Blood and guts being spread on bodies,
Violent crimes are being constantly committed.
Death to all who betray the king.
On a dark silent night, only an owl shrieking.
With unexplained mysteries hidden under
The night's watchful eye, he has been a betrayer.
Witchcraft haunts the withered air,
And unfolds the power lying on the heath.

Queens and kings are being killed,
Unpleasant prophecies are being fulfilled.

Sarah Parker (14)
Chigwell School, Chigwell

Friend Or Foe?

One small dagger, used to kill a man,
Murdered by the 'noble' soldier,
Successful in completing his prediction,
Promised to be ruler of the great land.
Led on by an accomplice,
Although the two had their doubts.

Honoured highly in the battle,
Both soldier and friend,
Fighting against the rebels,
Returning with victory on their side.
Also with a terrible traitor,
To be executed.

Kurran Gujral (13)
Chigwell School, Chigwell

Tsunami

Something so calm
But it's not nature
Little monster lurking
Then he starts a tantrum
Venom in his eyes
People look at the ominous sea
Faster and faster it flows
Until suddenly it erupts
Then he calms down
Unforgettable, horrible
Until next year

Suddenly erupts like a volcano
Beneath, below the water
Laid back and relaxed
Thrashing about in the water
Vicious sound he makes
Prancing around, noticing a change
Fleeing people run from the beach
Unforgivable disaster he caused
The massive destruction he caused
Undying pain in people's hearts
When he will throw his next
tantrum!

Alex Andrews (12)
Chigwell School, Chigwell

Paranoia

Up upon the blustery moor of torturing craving,
stand the enchanters of their molesting behaving,
Tormenting and abusing one's death-shaken head,
to lay their ambitions down to dead.
Blood and paranoia which feeds on a man,
so hungry for glory he shall never withstand
His eagerness and hunger to claim what is his,
the poor man used to their novelty persists.
How such an amulet can poison one's mind,
with enough bait to possess his ingenuity and find
What token he shall receive at the oppressing end,
shall be rusty and broken just like his end.

Elizabeth Van Maanen (13)
Chigwell School, Chigwell

41

Vamosk

Dark outside
Crack with the tail
Teeth sharp
Eats eels
Sips water
Fattens prey
Cunning like a fox
Creaks when you sleep
Legs, four of them
Two crooked faces
Ghastly and hated
Fast, never seen

doom in sight
crunch with the teeth
see the paw mark
leg it when you see it
slurps blood
feeds with care
flops when sleeps
thwacks when mad
flinches when sees a fly
can bite through a lion
hairy arms
flees when tried to be caught.

Sonal Ohrie (12)
Chigwell School, Chigwell

Time

Every day comes and goes:
A blink of the eye,
A sniff of the nose.

Every minute is so valuable:
To be remembered forever,
And to be cherished by all.

People wish time would last forever:
To gain new experiences,
But then today would seem like never.

Jason Driver (15)
Chigwell School, Chigwell

How I Feel about You!

Whenever you're near,
My heart is thumping,
I feel fear,
When I hear
Myself ask,
Will you be mine forever?

When I hear your voice,
I can't help but make no noise,
You fill me up with warmth.

When I hear your laughter,
I see your beauty,
On the inside and out.

The smell of your perfume,
The sparkle of your smile.

Mixed emotions every time,
And happiness shines,
But love shows more.

When you are near,
My heart is thumping,
I feel no fear!
When I hear your whisper,
Of course!

Kelly Wong (12)
Cleeve Park School, Sidcup

Cars

They're old, they're cold, they're full of mould.
They're new, there's two, they love me and you.
They come in all sorts of colours, but they don't have mothers.
They get lonely and they're the only one.
They make weird noses from little buttons.

Lennie Pearce (11)
Cleeve Park School, Sidcup

43

The Ocean

The ocean is as blue as the sky,
The fish are swimming,
High and low,
In the underwater life.

No limit of swimming, they are just fine,
All of the fish are swimming free,
The big sharks come from nowhere,
The little fish try to escape.

As the sharks come to eat,
All the fish go right now,
Before they get eaten,
In the underwater life.

The sharks are furious,
They are hungry,
They search again,
For more fish to eat.

Finally they catch some dinner,
As they chomp their way through,
They are now not hungry,
In the underwater life.

Billy Collins (12)
Cleeve Park School, Sidcup

Football

I'm standing in the tunnel
And I'm full of nerves
I have got a really good chance now
I'm playing for the reserves.

All I need to do now
Is just score a goal
If I do this
My face will not be dull.

Oliver Robinson (11)
Cleeve Park School, Sidcup

44

White Lions

White lions are fantastic,
They have beautiful fur
Even though the males are heavier
They have such brilliant manes.

They are such excellent predators,
But there are few of them left,
They are hunted for their fur,
But we are trying to stop that.

Lionesses do most of the hunting,
But the pride stays together.
One male dominates the pride
But their cubs are born blind.

They feed on grazing animals,
But rarely hunt at day.
They hunt at night,
But their lack of camouflage means they are easy to spot.

Their cubs are born blind,
But there are only about 30 left in the wild.
Their cubs are pure white,
But normal lion cubs are spotted.

Jack Needham (12)
Cleeve Park School, Sidcup

Snow

I fall in tiny pieces from the sky above,
I give the world a blanket, as white as a dove,
I'm bitterly cold throughout night or day,
Most prefer to stay inside, but others come out to play,
From the ground they pick me up, and turn me into a ball,
Then I'm thrown across the sky, I like that most of all,
Out pops a yellow ball, and melts me all away,
Bye-bye people, bye-bye world, I'll come another day!

Jamila Adi (12)
Cleeve Park School, Sidcup

45

Summer

The sun as hot as an oven,
shining its happiness
upon us.

The bees buzzing,
the butterflies fluttering
as the summer light glows.

Cold, mouth-watering and tasty,
the ice cream tastes.
Chocolatey, foamy
as the ice cream hits my tongue.

Screaming, shouting
as the children play.
Jumping, hopping
as they run away.

Slowly, quietly
the blanket of darkness
hovers over us.
The sun says goodbye
and the moon says hello.

Chanel Hayre (11)
Cleeve Park School, Sidcup

Untitled

When I see those big, soft balls fall
Down from the sky so very tall
I think about ping-pong balls
So white and round
Falling and tumbling to the ground.
That nasty hit
It was like I'd been bit
It was a snowball so very fast
It had almost put me in a cast
That's what I am talking about - *snow!*

Jack Aldridge (12)
Cleeve Park School, Sidcup

46

The Seasons

With everywhere covered in a white blanket,
Bare trees making me cold,
With the sun glistening majestically,
There's magic in the air.

When flowers bloom and trees blossom,
And birds sing again,
With a chilly breeze and a nice warm sun,
With bushes covered in leaves.

The sunny sun reflecting on the sea,
The grass swaying in time with the wind,
With ice cream, bathing in the sun,
The creatures are out and crawling about.

As it begins to fade, the time has come
And coldness strikes again,
The wind rustling the ruins,
To the top of the tree, to the last leaf on a twig.

It won't be long until summer's here again,
And so it will go on until time has reached its end.

Rachel Carabine-Clarke (12)
Cleeve Park School, Sidcup

Snow

Snow, snow, a wonderful thing,
I'll get my mates and give em a ring.

We'll go sledging at Danson Park,
It'll be great, we'll have a lark.

Going down hills at maximum speed,
It was real funny when we hit a tree.

Snowball fights on the football field,
I used a snowman as a loyal shield.

My friend pummelled me to the ground,
Onto a white blanket that reigned around.

I lay on a white blanket of snow
But it was so thick the grass did not show.

Snow, snow, a wonderful thing,
It's time for a rest until tomorrow
When I get to ring more friends.

Connor Holmes (12)
Cleeve Park School, Sidcup

Spring

When the harsh, cold and bitter winter has gone,
Spring comes to shine with us.
The crisp, fresh air glides in the atmosphere -
1, 2, 3, we breathe in and close our eyes.
We dream of flying, we dream of friendship,
We dream of everything . . . spring!
The pure white clouds float as a heaven on a sky-blue duvet.
The warm, bright sun glows on us softly.
Blossoms fall from green trees like sugar sprinkling on the soft grass.
Yellow, pink and blue butterflies fly in the air without a care.
The flowers bloom with different colours, so soft, such a sight!
We take in spring and pull it close to us like our own mother
And play with it for three glorious months.

Feyi Kadri (11)
Cleeve Park School, Sidcup

48

Seasons

Seasons are magical,
Seasons are bright.
Seasons are worrying,
Seasons are ripe.

Seasons are you,
Seasons are me.
We share them together,
We play in a tree.

Seasons end,
And seasons begin.
Seasons are different,
And seasons are within.

Emily North (12)
Cleeve Park School, Sidcup

My War

Big, black birds fly in the sky
people scream and run,
as houses are bursting into flames
the sirens are screaming loud.

Evacuation is going on.
children are sent away,
it's time for parents to wave goodbye
to keep their children safe.

The shelters are not safe anymore
as the fire is quickly spreading,
all you hear are screams and shouts
of people slowly dying.

Lucy Cutting (12)
Cleeve Park School, Sidcup

49

Sonnet To My Love
(Based on 'Sonnet 18' by Shakespeare)

Shall I compare thee to the sparkling sea?
Thou art more beautiful than a day of spring
Rough seas do shake my passion for thee
Then the tide goes and my passion stays steady
Sometimes too cold to go in the sea
And then the tide makes you drift away
And then I go out to swim and find thee
But it is worth it when I find thee
But thou immortal sea keeps leeching the passion from thee
Even though I try hard to catch up with thee
My passion for thee keeps me going
But my passion dies as I lose my faith
But as long as I live I keep on going
And I shall find thee eventually.

Willliam Hanshaw Green (12)
Colchester High School, Colchester

A Sonnet For My Love . . .
(Based on 'Sonnet 18' by Shakespeare)

Shall I compare thee to a Christmas Day?
Full of happiness and joy,
In every single way,
Where we are given loads of lovely toys.
You are as cool as the snow on the grass,
Yet you feel as warm as a sunny day,
I hope this Christmas is not our last,
To ruin our excitable ways,
This day just goes too fast,
As we are all so cheerful and gay,
We put our peaceful banner on the mast,
You are as beautiful as the sun's rays,
I hope our love will last forever,
And we will always be together.

Emily Bowyer (12)
Colchester High School, Colchester

My Sonnet
(Based on 'Sonnet 18' by Shakespeare)

Shall I compare thee to the shining stars?
Thou art more peaceful and so gentle, calm
Though the clouds can dim the lovely brightness
And the quiet night is all too short
Sometimes the frost is horribly biting
And often the silver is not displayed
You are so lovely, sweeter than the night
And you are nature's gift, you stand so calm
But thy beautiful stars shall never fade
Nor ever be robbed of that beauty
Nor shall the burning stare raise your beauty
When in the future you shall always be
So the ears of Man hear your calm voice
And the eyes can see you shine and glitter.

Rebecca Harvey (11)
Colchester High School, Colchester

Sonnet To My Love
(Based on 'Sonnet 18' by Shakespeare)

Shall I compare thee to the stars in the sky?
Thou art more beautiful than a rose in the spring
Rough winds do snap the petals of May
And summer's up-commence does end in a flash
Sometimes too hot, the glass of the sky shines
And often the shiny substance dims
And from moon to moon it declines
By chance we meet together unknown
But our immortal love shall not fade
Nor lose the love we feel together
Nor shall death bring us apart
When together we only feel the beat of our hearts
So long as I can breathe and see you
So I live, and this gives life to thee

Nathan Moss (12)
Colchester High School, Colchester

51

My Sonnet
(Based on 'Sonnet 18' by Shakespeare)

Shall I compare thee to a flower
On a beautiful summer's day?
When you are in season you have so much power,
Especially in May,
Your stem is so green
And your bud is so yellow,
So you cannot be seen,
Not by a mortal fellow.
Your petals are so cool,
Reminding me of unusual passion.
They're like a swimming pool,
Because of your fashion.
I shall preserve this love of ours forever,
Because in my mind we'll always be together.

Liam Martin (11)
Colchester High School, Colchester

My Love Poem
(Based on 'Sonnet 18' by Shakespeare)

Shall I compare thee to an autumn day?
Golden and orange leaves all around me.
Bare trees stripped of leaves left on the ground,
let nature do its bit for winter months.
Crispy mornings, days on end through winter,
cold mornings coming to an end today.
But don't worry, spring is now on its way,
bulbs and white snowdrops sprouting in the soil.
Spring is over, come with me to summer,
we can sit together while we watch a lake.
Flowing gently to its wonderful wake,
this is to you my wonderful, great one.

Elliott Mo (11)
Colchester High School, Colchester

52

A Poem To My Loved One
(Based on 'Sonnet 18' by Shakespeare)

Shall I compare you to the sun?
I shine bright, you melt me entirely
In the summer like a sticky bun
I am like a door and you are my key
The sun shines bright when I see you
But disappears when you go away from me
In the summer flowers thrive
But die in winter because of the cold
When you kiss me my heart does a jive
I will be courageous and be very bold
To ask for your hand in marriage
And to leave in a bright white carriage.

Thomas Lucey (12)
Colchester High School, Colchester

A Poem For My Love
(Based on 'Sonnet 18' by Shakespeare)

Shall I compare thee to a spring morning?
Thou art a loving end to winter
Thou art like a morning chorus
Thou art new life of spring
Thou art happy warmth from the sun
Thou are like Mother Nature
Thou hast a thousand suns
Loving and caring
And thou art a soft breeze on a warm day
Rough winds may blow
But our love stands tall.

Josh Lucking (11)
Colchester High School, Colchester

Poem To My Love
(Based on 'Sonnet 18' by Shakespeare)

Shall I compare thee to the beautiful night sky?
Thou are more lovely and more forgiving
Tsunami Victoria sinks Venice down
And day takes over the sparkling night
Sometimes too dark the lovely night sky is
Often its silvery substance is dimmed
By chance or destiny we meet each other
But our strong love shall not ever start to fade
Nor lose possession of that starry sky
Nor shall break us apart
Where immortal life will keep us together.

James Murrell (12)
Colchester High School, Colchester

Nightmares

N ormally, I find in the middle of the night
I have happy dreams, I never have a fright
G ood news, however, is not always present
H ours of nightmares are never very pleasant
T o understand the worry of this scary situation
M y dreams you will have to visit, this is not an overreaction
A dream is like a mini life, you're free to do what you wish
R arely, though, it happens, it swims away like a fish
E very night I worry there is an ominous gloom
S o get prepared in the night if you hear a sudden boom!

James Lavender (11)
Colchester High School, Colchester

54

My Poem To Rugby
(Based on 'Sonnet 18' by Shakespeare)

Shall he be compared to a towering wall?
The posts rattle still from a hero's drop kick,
There's no one harder than him on the ball,
Unlike footballers, rugby players are intelligent not thick.

Rugby is the game, the game of skill,
The players are tough and quick on the pitch,
They are not fazed by the gruesome blood spill,
Cuts, no big deal, to be fixed with a stitch.

Adam Cook (11)
Colchester High School, Colchester

Icicles

Icicles are the fangs of a wolf;
Bared in readiness, prepared to engulf.

Icicles are the claws of a witch;
Scratching your windows, sounding menacingly high pitch.

Icicles are the thorns on a rose;
Waiting to prick you, a small threat they pose.

Icicles are the jagged rocks of a cliff face;
Whose serrated edges claw at an empty space.

Icicles are the bare branches of a tree;
Through which moonlight seeps past, causing rats to flee.

Icicles are the chills down your spine;
Tingles that race down, shaped like the needles of a pine.

Maya Le-Yao Thompson (13)
Dartford Grammar School for Girls, Dartford

55

Shadows

His head always looks down, never up.
His hood is constantly hanging over his face.
He wears gloves, long jumpers and jeans to cover every bit
of his skin.
He is just a shadow and nothing more.

A whisper never leaves his lips, during school he just sits in the far
corner, dreaming of a better life.
He has no friends, no family to talk to,
He is alone in this world and no foster family can amend that.
He is just a shadow and nothing more.

He walks home with not a soul by his side; the only bit of life
that lives in him is his music.
Each night he sits on his bed wondering, why me . . . ? What did I do
to deserve this life? Why can't I just be a beautiful pale white?
He is just a shadow and nothing more.

He never eats breakfast, lunch or dinner, because of him life
is a pointless cycle.
He can't smile, he can't show excitement, just sorrow.
He is just a shadow and nothing more.

White and black are completely opposite colours . . . but so are
blue and orange and yet they can contrast with each other
in paintings.
Colours are all different and have unique meanings to each.
Humans, on the other hand, share the same nature.
and that is what counts.

Beat racism!

Eleisha Rai (14)
Dartford Grammar School for Girls, Dartford

Red

You think it's worse, I think it's better,
You think it's pain, I think it's pleasure,
You think it's wrong, I think it's right,
You think it hurts, but really it doesn't,
At least not so much as this.
Pain isn't blood dripping down my leg,
It's banging my head against that wall for thinking I need you.
It's being trapped in this hopeless tower,
Walls closing in,
No windows,
No door.
It's throwing myself off this roof,
The adrenaline burning up inside me,
Until it all burns out,
And it doesn't hurt anymore.
Everything is nothing,
And nothing is blackness,
Blackness is red,
Red is blood,
Blood is my release,
Blood is my hope,
My anger,
My grief,
My life.

Georgia Roach (14)
Dartford Grammar School for Girls, Dartford

Dark Emotion

Loneliness creeps in my soul
The night as black as fire coal
Sadness lurking in my head
As I lay alone in bed
Darkness crawls across my face
My fear is spreading all over the place.

Robyn Heather (11)
Dartford Grammar School for Girls, Dartford

True Friend

You're a true friend
And I want you to know,
Our love for each other
Has helped us grow.

If I could catch a rainbow,
I'd do it just for you,
And share with you its beauty
On the days you're feeling blue.

At the end of the tunnel,
You'll be my guiding light,
You'll lead me up to Heaven
And bid me goodnight.

We'll be there together,
And we'll never grow old,
And we'll walk hand in hand
On the streets of paved gold.

And when the time comes,
That we're put to our rest,
Be sure that you know
You're the very best!

Maroua Benterkia (12)
Dartford Grammar School for Girls, Dartford

Tranquillity

There was a male,
Not only was he a male, he was a hippy,
So, he was very pale,
Sitting by the warm, steep sea,

As light, bright blue as the sky,
The sapphire sea is a fish,
As the sun shone and gleamed on the sea,
Making little colourful diamonds.

I saw not one rock,
But lots of rocks sitting on the beach,
The smell of the salty sea,
Hearing the waves splashing.

Wearing some tattered skinny trousers,
With a green grassy shirt,
White clear glasses that he was wearing,
He had short hair,

The smile on his face,
Looking at the graceful dolphins jump and cross over,
Beautiful doves flying over him,
While the sun is a soothing orange.

Mathura Balakrishnan (13)
Dartford Grammar School for Girls, Dartford

59

Rain And Rain

Rain is sometimes a child, an impatient child,
Just as you have finished your shopping and on the way home,
It hits you like a bombshell and gets you soaked
Like a sponge dipped into a bucket of cold water,
It stops but just can't wait and bursts out into song.

Rain is sometimes an adult, an angry adult,
Just as you have finished putting out the washing,
It targets you and thumps around, darting lumps of water,
Commanding you to get as wet as the ocean,
It carries on, blowing the washing around, roaring and shouting.

Sometimes rain acts like both adult and child,
Just as things are getting better it happens all over again.

Lawuratu Sanda-Bah (12)
Dartford Grammar School for Girls, Dartford

Stop

Stop hanging off my branches, my many twisted arms,
Stop knocking down my conkers, you troublesome little bairns.
Stop killing all my brothers, for paper and for fire,
Stop taking from my sister, for your rubber car tyres.
Stop driving from my bosom, the many little creatures,
Stop ripping up my elders, my fathers, my teachers.
Stop taking down my apples, and claiming them as yours,
Stop bringing in your big machines with their wide flashing jaws.
Stop tearing down my land, and replacing it with stone,
Stop chopping up my children, for your little wooden throne.

Fern Pitty (14)
Dartford Grammar School for Girls, Dartford

6o

The Uninquisitive Genius

'Ha ha!' cries the uninquisitive genius
'I suppose I just like to eat hands!'

'What?' says the ever avid intern
who stops and panics and stands.

As the tea gushed downstairs, the phone
began to ring and the genius started to sing:

'Phones! Phones are so romantic!'
And began his discussion on bread.

Poor avid intern fumed and turned
to go to bed.

'Halt! It's Sunday, you could be under arrest
if you try to get dressed!'

'Darn you, uninquisitive genius, it's you
that I detest . . .

I'm leaving for Bombay and for a living
I shall play the mandalay!'

'Mandalay? That's a place you incompetent fool,
go take a dip in a toxic pool!'

'You know I don't believe you're a genius
at all!'

Scarlette Alder Jimenez (13)
Friends' School (Study Centre), Saffron Walden

There Will Always Be Me

Now I have been crushed,
My heart turned to dust,
I do not know who to trust,
My life is sorrow.

However much thy willow may weep,
I will always love you,
And if another man you seek,
I will always love you.

If you may not love,
That is your choice,
But you are like a dove,
You make us rejoice.

Thy pain stings me,
Like a hornet or a bee,
If you find another love, let joy be free,
And if he crushes your heart,
There will always be me.

Joshua Garwood (12)
Friends' School (Study Centre), Saffron Walden

Alone

The trees streaked by,
The wind stung my eyes,
The blood pounded in my head,
The ground tore at my feet,
I was alone.

Winter's cold breath harms us all,
Spring's flowers bloom just to die,
Summer's heat is crude,
Autumn's leaves crunch and break,
I am alone.

As you run from the hunter,
As you gasp for breath,
As you stop and pause,
As you know you're going to die,
I will always be alone.

Frances White (11)
Friends' School (Study Centre), Saffron Walden

The Empty Chair

A hundred days ago he left for war,
uneasy in ill-fitting desert kit.
A swift kiss for his wife, whose eyes were raw,
then he clutched the chair in which he loved to sit.
'Keep my chair warm for me till I come back.'
Then he's off to face the desert and the sun
and the silent foe who waits among the black
of deepest shadows, with his rusty gun.
He learns to take the anger and the hate
as arid as the unforgiving sun,
and grows to trust the judgement of his mates
who watch his back until patrol is done.
But wife and chair will wait for him in vain
as his blood stains steaming sands like scarlet rain.

Harry Blackmore (15)
Friends' School (Study Centre), Saffron Walden

63

A Woman Such As Me

Are you scared of monsters hiding 'neath your bed
Or scared of the darkness residing in your head?
Or maybe fright is caused by pain from another
I tell you there's nothing quite as frightful as an unrelenting lover.

Handsome in features, sweet as sugared pie,
Would catch the attention of ladies, as soon as he passed by
He left nothing but a shadow upon Heaven's gate
Told me in our wedding bed, for him I should wait.

He could not help but indulge in his love of human art
And all the while the Devil consumed his merry heart.
Passionate hatred came to rest within my soul
I watched him with steady gaze, eyes as black as coal.

I did not remember I had hold of the knife
Nor did I remember that I was his loyal wife.
I do remember the sound of his flesh splitting open
His red blood spilling to the ground, his unhappy token.

His prize collection still hangs upon my dusty wall,
But the portrait of his younger days still tops them all.
Never again will I marry, one with fanciful demeanour
Who believes that his model will be his sweet redeemer.

I ask myself the question, did I possess his love?
No, I answer in the same breath, for he was like a dove.
A dove is pure, a dove is free, a dove is graceful as was he
Still I had to make him see
He didn't belong to anyone, but me.

Are you scared of monsters hiding 'neath your bed
Or scared of the darkness residing in your head?
If you plan to be faithful, then blessed you will be
But if the Devil consumes your heart, then soon you will see
That there's nothing quite as frightful, as a woman such as me.

Jade Hawkey (16)
Gravesend Grammar School for Girls, Gravesend

 64

Innocence

O' why doth the world steal thy innocence?
Snatch it so cruelly, leaving reality to engulf thee.
Thy hearts become polluted with the corruption of Man,
And thou must weep for thy children.

Hath the young wolves of innocence, desires untold?
That become lost through thy sinful world of hate.
O'er corruption doth thy desires lie forgotten?
Hast thou mislaid thy memory of old?

Thou have grown in ignorance of thy loss,
And hath sleepeth through the dawn of sin.
O'er seas of green hath the young wolves run,
Leaveth thou corruption and fly with freedom.

Doth the winds of change resound in thy land?
Calling the young to flee to lands of myth.
O' innocence has been stolen from thy grip,
And thy Lord weepeth for thy loss.

O' why doth the world steal thy innocence?
Snatch it so cruelly, leaving reality to engulf thee.
Thy young wolves hath been polluted with sin,
And thy childish desires lie sleeping in thy hearts.

Charlotte Johnson (17)
Gravesend Grammar School for Girls, Gravesend

Autism

A tightly shut mouth with wide open ears
A silent voice of a thousand words
A habit of strict routine, not to be broken
A lack of clear instruction yet carries the job out with maximum effort
An unpopular character with amazing and unique interests
A musician with no skill but always feels the rhythm
A seemingly 'hopeless' puzzle-solving genius
A traveller who takes the different path to everyone else
An emotionless outer shell hiding a caring hero
A person that can read others' emotions yet not his own
An eternal barrier blocking a heart of gold.

Connor Giannandrea (14)
Hayes School, Hayes

66

Without You

Give me water and I shall cleanse you,
Even if the air is thick with acrid filth.
Give me wings and I will fly to the ends of the Earth,
Even if the sky collapses into the dark water.
Give me blood and I may give life,
Even if the dead roam and weep grey tears.
Give me your love and I will leap to glaze in it,
Even if hate grips my heart and grinds it black.
Because without you,
There is no lust.
Without you
There is no emotion.
No sin.
No passion.
No Heaven.
No Hell.
Because without you,
There is no heart within me.
I surrender my being to you
So that just for even a second, you can give me your heart
So that we can resonate as one.
This is my gift to you.
My vow.

Pape Gueye (17)
Helena Romanes School, Great Dunmow

World War II Poem

I long to feel the cool summer breeze on my hot face,
For the wind to play with my hair.
I long to see the daffodils and birds,
To see the bunnies hop about in the green grass.
I wish to taste the refreshing coolness of ice cream,
To taste the freshness in fresh fruit.

We people haven't seen daylight for ages,
We've been stuck in this metal shelter;
Our hearts pounding whenever we hear footsteps outside,
Worrying about the world, our friends and family,
Waiting for news, or something to put our minds at ease.
Wanting to know that we are safe, and will be reunited
With our loved ones soon.

It all started the night we heard the siren,
Panicking I woke my family up, hurrying them along.
We were halfway to the shelter when I lost my family,
Pushed towards the shelter, I called for them,
Desperate and upset, my heart felt as if it was torn into pieces.
And then I knew, I would never see them again.
I was alone.

Now I'm sitting in the shelter, writing this poem.
My feet hurt from searching the crowds for my family, with no luck,
Feeling more alone than ever.
But wait . . . what's that?
Is it . . . could it possibly be . . .
The all-clear siren?

We emerge from the shelter, to come face to face
With complete devastation,
Our eyes are stinging from the bright sunlight.
I walk over to my house, now reduced to rubble and stones.
People are crying, hugging, some children are just sitting on the floor,
Staring into space.
I know how they feel, and it hurts.
I walk over to join them, and my world collapses.

Chloe Duncan (12)
Holmesdale Technology College, Snodland

68

WWII

The sirens have gone off, it is time to run,
I gasp for the air as I hear a sudden bang,
The smoke's behind me like a black forest,
I see a little boy all alone; nobody with him.
I start to sing a hymn,
The hymn for hope, nothing else,
I look back for one last glimpse of normality,
My house has been blown to pieces.
I get pushed to the floor by the rushing, scared people,
I attempt to get up while no one is around.

I run to the shelter and sit in the corner,
No sign of anyone I know,
Then a well-known voice calls for me, it is my sister,
I cuddle her hard, trying not to cry,
Mum and Dad perished in the explosion,
The whole community starts to sing for hope.
I hear the planes flying over our heads,
The all-safe siren goes off; peace for all,
I go outside with my sister, like I am stuck to her with glue.

All we see are people crying with fear,
Nowhere to go, me or my sister,
We follow everyone else to their remains,
We see pieces of houses on the floor,
Photos, clothes, people's lives,
Where is everyone?
Where are the local places?
I see people here, I see people there,
Me and my sister stagger to our house,
The house in pieces, our belonging scattered about,
We go to our family's houses,
Nobody there,
Where is the community spirit?
Where is everyone?

Rebecca French (12)
Holmesdale Technology College, Snodland

Will I Go Home?

Clutching my teddy bear and little brown bag,
Not wanting to let go of my mother's hand,
But if I don't go I might only breathe once more,
I'm going away.

I've got a tag around my neck,
And I feel all alone,
Bombs are coming, and I must escape,
I'm going away.

It's as if the 'bad men' have taken my joy,
But I know I must stay firm,
No more running from my bed to the shelter,
I'm going away.

Waiting in line,
Waiting to be selected,
Will no one want me?
I'm here to stay.

I've been chosen now and feeling better,
Still miss Mummy,
But I'm all right,
I'm here to stay.

Life's better now,
And Mummy writes,
I'm doing my foremost,
I'm here to stay.

I've been away for three years now,
And I'm beginning to get worried,
I want information,
What's happening?
Is my mother OK?
Will I go home?

Lucy Ventham (12)
Holmesdale Technology College, Snodland

70

Women Of World War II

We are the women of World War II,
Spending our spare time, renewing ageing shoes,
We're doing the jobs which are meant for men,
Oh, we really do wonder when
Life as we knew it will return;
Waiting for the bombers to learn.

We are the women of World War II,
Attempting to cope without you.
The siren is screaming and loud,
We have to get to the shelter in the ground,
We don't know when we'll come out,
Babies cry and children shout.

We are the women of World War II,
All the time we never knew
If you would be coming home,
As bright as the stars in the night sky roam.
I hope and pray you're alive,
Come back to life and we'll thrive.

We are the women of World War II,
Do you miss me as much as I miss you?
In my spare time, all I do is cry,
Sitting alone and wondering why
You had to go to war;
You've left my heart wounded and sore.

We are the women of World War II,
You stay strong for me, and I'll stay strong for you.
Some whisper and some scream
But you are the topic of my dreams.
The war is hard, but soon it will be gone
Because, let's face it, you've been away too long.

Jessie Walton (12)
Holmesdale Technology College, Snodland

71

I Stand, I Sit, I Talk, I Scream

I stand, I sit, I talk, I scream,
Yet everything I try to do does not take away the pain.
My life is demolished and many are the same;
The faces of others show devastation.
Yet I cannot worry about others because

I stand, I sit, I talk, I scream,
Yet everything I try to do does not take away the pain.
I sit alone; like a soldier in the trenches
I hear loud noises, screaming, shouting, crying.
I have thoughts of my family dying.

I stand, I sit, I talk, I scream,
Yet everything I try to do does not take away the pain.
I try to sleep but I cannot
Because just as I do, I hear a gunshot.
I can feel everyone's pain.
Everybody feels the same.

I stand, I sit, I talk, I scream,
Yet everything I try to do does not take away the pain.
The sirens suddenly stop;
The room goes silent . . .
People creep up from where they are sitting . . .

I stand, I sit, I talk, I scream,
Yet everything I try to do does not take away the pain.
I step outside, the fresh air blows against my face,
Dirt and rubble irritate my eyes.
My house!
My house!
It's
Gone . . .

Jessica Worsfold (12)
Holmesdale Technology College, Snodland

I Sit In Silence

I sit in silence
Until I hear
The screams.
The sounds of the planes flying overhead
Like a whirling tornado.

I sit in silence
Until I hear
The screams.
The flickering of the candle attracts my gaze
Like a moth to a light.

I sit in silence
Until I hear
The screams.
The house is gone
And all of my belongings.

I sit in silence
Until I hear
The screams.
Surrounded by strangers,
Not knowing
What has happened
To my family?
Will I ever see them again?

I sit in silence
Until I hear
The screams.
Crowded shelters and babies
Crying.
I sit in silence until I hear the screams.

Chloe Lewin (12)
Holmesdale Technology College, Snodland

Sitting Alone

There I was sitting alone, holding back the tears as they came,
The look on everybody's faces as I looked around,
The sound of the constant drilling of the air raid siren
Running through my head,
My vision becoming blurred as my eyes filled with tears.

When all of a sudden I heard an explosion
From outside as I felt myself
Becoming paralysed,
The feeling that was growing inside of me was becoming unbearable,
The temperature of the bunker rising every minute
As more and more people tried to cram inside.

Then the sound of the air raid siren ringing through my ears
Finally stopped, although I knew that it was far from over.
I started to panic more and more, listening to the sound of
Everyone's voices blurring into one,
I was listening out for the one voice I was desperate to hear,
But there was nothing.
I tried to breathe although I only ended up breathing in smoke
As it filled up my aching lungs,
As I grew more and more tense by the minute,
Wondering whether this nightmare would ever end.

I closed my eyes trying to calm myself down,
Trying to block out the outside noise,
As I heard footsteps approaching me,
I felt my heart start to pump five times faster,
As wonderful thoughts came into my head,
I opened my eyes, only to find a family coming to fill up a gap.

Lorna Mills (12)
Holmesdale Technology College, Snodland

74

War Poem

The siren sounds,
It's here again,
Quickly grabbing my gas mask,
Sprinting rapidly to the shelter.

A massive blast,
And suddenly I'm knocked flying through the air,
An explosion of smoke blurs my vision,
Where is everyone?

I struggle to get to my feet,
Crying all the time,
All I can hear is the siren,
It's killing me inside,
All this bombing is horrendous.

I fall into the shelter,
Trying to catch my breath,
Looking for my family,
All I can hear now are screams of small children.

Suddenly my name gets called,
But am I just imagining it?
There are people crowded around me,
Half them I don't know.

Most of the night has passed,
I'm still looking for my family,
My heart is tensing as I don't know what to feel,
Am I going to find them?

Carly Harding (12)
Holmesdale Technology College, Snodland

I See, I Hear, I Feel, I Know

I see rushing people,
I hear the sirens,
I feel very afraid,
I know it's time.

My family tell me,
It's going to be okay.
I wish, if only,
They were here to tell me now.

I am alone in the countryside,
Without my real family.
But I know I am safe,
I just don't believe it.

I am under the shelter,
I can hear the bombs nearby.
I think of all the families,
Who have lost everything.

The sirens have ended,
I step outside.
I stand alone,
In front of my demolished home.

I see a destroyed town,
I hear silence.
I feel upset,
I have lost everything.

Lauren Harrison (13)
Holmesdale Technology College, Snodland

Pompeii

The sky was filled with ashes,
That fell from the dark night,
Children were no longer dreaming,
People ran with fright.

A rumble from the mountain,
Shook from all around,
Screams filled the air,
But the mountain drowned their sound.

Gold hot sparks fell down,
Down from the above,
And fell on innocent victims,
All of them praying for love.

Then came another rumble,
This time lava poured out,
It raced down the hill towards them,
No wonder they all had doubt.

Death was soon coming,
Across the river it fled,
Every boy and girl,
Man and woman, would soon be dead.

Now they are frozen in time,
Statues every one,
People come and visit,
Disasters had only begun!

Amy Gearing (12)
Holmesdale Technology College, Snodland

Destroyed

The silence shields the dark night,
I lie reflecting on the day that has just passed,
I feel a heavy shudder,
Sirens break the silence,
Loud screams take over the darkness.

My mother grabbed my weak arm,
Taking me to the front door,
She whispered, 'Shelter,' in my ear,
I ran as fast as my legs could run
Towards the busy shelter.

A sudden noise came from my house;
So loud it knocked me off my feet,
I couldn't look back,
Not to see my past destroyed.

I crawled towards the shelter,
I stepped in; seeing crowds of people,
I searched the crowds for family, like a lost child,
I sat in the corner with tears running down my cheeks.
Waiting for the noises to stop was dreadful,
I wanted to go home to family and friends.

The shelter doors opened wide,
Fresh air poured in,
I looked outside to see the town demolished,
My house destroyed . . . !

Hannah Long (13)
Holmesdale Technology College, Snodland

78

World War II

As I run, I don't look back,
I want to know that I'll be safe.
Why can't I find anyone?
Anyone that will help me.
I scream but no one listens
Help!

I follow the hustle and bustle of the crowd,
But as I do I feel my feet are swept from underneath me.
No one cared, they just trampled over me
Like I was another piece of dirt scattered from the trenches.
As I looked around it wasn't a dream, it was all genuine
Help!

I knew I needed to get up but I couldn't move
My legs had been crushed
But someone hauled me up and put me on their shoulder
All I could hear in my ear was the siren so loud
It was deafening me but all I could think of was my family
Help!

As we got in the shelter the stranger slumped me down
But as I looked around, it was not a stranger, Mum!
We got shoved and bumped
So we got into the corner and cuddled up
Waiting for the all clear siren
Feeling safe!

Anna Gibbs-Murray (12)
Holmesdale Technology College, Snodland

9/11

I never thought this day would come,
Where everybody's heart was filled with glum.
I'd thought I would never die,
But the person who made it happen told a lie!
He was a horrible person,
And killed millions of people.

Where people were terrified,
Where families were petrified,
From seeing their family being burnt,
And that person should have learnt.
Nobody knew why it happened,
The people were saddened.

I never thought this day would come,
Where everybody's heart was filled with glum.
I thought I would never die,
But the person who made it happen told a lie!
He was a horrible person,
And killed millions of people.

Nobody ever spoke of it again,
Because people didn't want the memories again.
Still people will not forget.
But put their minds to rest.
The buildings were a wreck,
And the people who were there, their life was heck.

Amber Hayward (11)
Holmesdale Technology College, Snodland

8o

My Life In This Shelter

You hear the siren,
It's the same routine,
Sprinting to the shelter,
For the third time,
When is it going to end?

Nothing is ever safe,
In this harsh world of explosions.
The Germans are coming.
Turn the lights off and be quiet,
Settle down for the night,
It's going to be a long one
When is it going to end?

Some high-pitched screams,
Telling them to be quiet,
So we can listen out for the siren,
It's still going on.
When is it going to end?

On the night of this elongated day,
Everyone is asleep . . . apart from me,
Worrying about loads of things,
How can other people sleep?

A million and one things rushing through my head,
Seriously, when is it going to end?

Stanley Brooks (12)
Holmesdale Technology College, Snodland

Untitled

Smoke and dust everywhere,
The sound of whistling bombs,
The sirens still making a noise.
There are lots of little girls and boys
Running to the shelter,
And screaming.

The damp-smelling air
Of the air raid shelter
All cramped.

It has been a couple of hours now
And all the bombs are still on the prowl.
All the lights are still off.
All the children are in the country.
I can hear all the bombs dropping outside;
They get nearer and nearer.

The sirens are gradually stopping now,
Everybody's face looks more cheerful
Now the bombing's over.

But the devastation is tremendous.
My house is nothing anymore
Just rubble and dust.

Bradley Harris (12) & Mia Harris
Holmesdale Technology College, Snodland

The Never-Ending War

I was sitting in the kitchen, eating a gorgeous dinner,
But then it was time to go to the air raid shelter.
The bang and the sirens going off all around me,
All of my family huddled together.

My dad and I ran as fast as we could,
My mum and brother crouching like old hags.
My heart was beating faster and louder
Like an elephant running away from its predator.

Trying not to think of what would happen,
The tears in my eyes were like a tap dripping louder and louder,
Up in the sky the planes swooped by,
Dropping the bombs from up high.

Everyone was coming in the air raid shelter,
My family and I were getting even closer.
The bombs came down, getting closer and closer to me,
Now I am thinking; would I ever need a key?

I was sitting in the kitchen eating a gorgeous dinner,
But then it was time to go to the air raid shelter.
The bang and the sirens going off all around me,
All of my family huddled together.

Elleshia Bridger (12)
Holmesdale Technology College, Snodland

83

WWII Poem!

It was dinner time,
The kids were hungry and wanted some food,
I began to drift into a depressing mood.

The kids were arguing - I needed some help,
I turned around and gave out a yelp!
I called down Tommy - the oldest one,
He was my only beautiful son,
I began to feel he was the only one I could rely on,
All of a sudden, a piercing sound - the air raid siren!

I grabbed the kids and ran for my life,
I dropped the plates and cut myself with a knife!

The Earth shook,
I turned around to have a look,
My joy and pride,
Little Victoria asked if I was OK, I lied!

My house was gone,
The great heap of rubble was gleaming,
The kids were screaming,
I had to get to the shelter in time,
For the kids, because they were mine!

Gemma Barden (11)
Holmesdale Technology College, Snodland

What's Happening?

The siren stops,
I crawl out from the rubble,
The smoke rises high,
The war is causing trouble.

A baby cries,
It's a terrible sound,
When I crept round,
No house could be found.

There are holes in the street,
There is an awful smell,
Last night what did happen?
When the bombs fell.

The train is off the tracks,
It has made a mess,
If Hitler surrenders,
The whole world would say, 'Yes!'

World War II is tiring,
We don't have the strength to carry on,
I wish the firing would stop,
It will make rations go out of the shop.

Craig Bailey (12)
Holmesdale Technology College, Snodland

The Young Soldier
(Poem based on the story of Frederick Robert Mills)

There was a young soldier aged fifteen
Who lied to get into the army in World War I
The boy was so young but he did not look his age
All the other soldiers said he looked seventeen
They did not care about his age
The only thing they cared about was
That they had more soldiers.
The young boy trained and trained.
The day came, he was going to be a soldier.
He was very nervous and knew that there was a possibility
That he could die. As he lined up to go to war,
The king himself gave them all a cigar.
The young soldier did not smoke.
They set off to go to war.
As the young boy set off, a bomb came down from the sky
And landed right in front of him.
Pieces came off the bomb and went into him.
He was really badly injured and could not fight.
He would have to wear a girdle for the rest of his life

Reiss Robert Mills (13)
Holmesdale Technology College, Snodland

War!

All I can hear is the noise of pain
All I can see is suffering
All I can touch is the remains of people's lives
All I can smell is the scent of war
My time is spent on figuring out my emotions
Life goes on, times change,
People become different,
Personalities fade, friends are forgotten

But my childhood will forever remain the same.

Bethany Sally-Ann Cradduck (13)
Holmesdale Technology College, Snodland

Sirens

Why was my mum shaking?
She doesn't normally;
Then this noise,
I'm not sure what it was
But Mum and Dad rose to their feet
And were rushing around
Then explained.

Now I know what a cave is.
So there we were, cramped in the shelter.
Bang! Crashes everywhere.
Were my friends okay?
I wanted to know!
Would this ever end?
I hoped.
Was this the end?
As we lay cramped, scared,
Wondering what was going on;
I really wanted to know.

Harry Hennon (13)
Holmesdale Technology College, Snodland

It's Safe

Sirens are wailing all around me,
I rip down the drooping curtains and stare into the bleak distance.

Across the road I can see the remains of a blown-up tree,
I start sprinting towards the door.
The sky is covered with the outlines of Nazi planes
Like a swarm of wasps covering the sky.

All over London there are shattered remains.
I go to the shelter, it's cramped and unhygienic,
But at least it's safe.
I have one final look at my home; as I turn, I hear a bang!

And finally I hear the iron door slam.

Mitchell Rae (13)
Holmesdale Technology College, Snodland

87

Tit For Tat

I met a young man, who had an experience he would never forget
He was brave and strong and had a lot of courage
But his life wasn't great. His friends were left for dead.

Rations, belts and no clean clothes or clean bed sheets
He would never answer back
He stared out of his window
As the soldiers marched in fleets.

Days went on and soldiers died
Bombs went off
And birds stopped flying
He and his mum sat in the shelter
And the little lad didn't stop crying.

His mum said, 'Tit for tat.'
The planes flew past but something was dropped
There was a scream and a shout
It all went dark and dusty
And for him that was that!

Abby-Louise Goodall (13)
Holmesdale Technology College, Snodland

Michael Jackson

J ackson was a superstar.
A flicker of light in a car.
C atching notes in and out.
K ing of Pop, a wandering scout.
S inging even though he's gone.
O nly gone in our minds.
N ever gone, always here.

Paige Baker (11)
Holmesdale Technology College, Snodland

Tsunamis, Help!

Here it comes, the big wave,
There is nothing to be saved.
Run, run as fast as you can.

People running and screaming
Water crashing so fast
'Help me! Help me!'
Is all you can hear.

Boats and cars flying everywhere,
Everyone does care.
Mother Nature at her worst.

Next day, people cry,
They look low, they look high.
Bodies lie in the street,
You see a hand twitching under a car.

People cry,
'Help! Help!'

Ellie Bailey (12)
Holmesdale Technology College, Snodland

Trenches

I'm in a trench
I'm trapped in by a fence
I can't get out
They won't hear me if I shout

They see me in a corner crying
They shoot me down and now I'm dying
Then I try to get up and start walking
And then I try to start talking

Then I see a bomb
My friend Tom picked up the bomb
And he chucked it out of the trench
And over the fence.

Kristian Barnes (13)
Holmesdale Technology College, Snodland

89

Just War!

I hear bombs and guns!
I see planes!
They think it's all games!
But they don't know what it is like!

I hear cries and screams!
I see death!
It's like a big war of theft!
But they don't know how it feels!

I hear the Nazis and the British!
I see smoke!
I feel broke!
But they feel no guilt!

I wonder if I'll survive!
What will happen?
Just one ambition!
I will kill Adolf Hitler!

Marc Chatfield (12)
Holmesdale Technology College, Snodland

Twin Towers

Imagine standing in New York
Hearing people scream not talk
Children crying, ambulances running,
The Twin Towers have been knocked down.

People have died and people are injured
It's a shame for our loss
See the Twin Towers falling quickly but slowly
They stood in the sky tall and proud.

The people who have destroyed our elegant view
Are becoming proud of what they have done
People have lost members of their family
Smoke is racing all over the city.

Kirsten Kirby (13)
Holmesdale Technology College, Snodland

My World War II Poem

I am five years old
I am sitting in the air raid shelter
I am wondering, wondering where my mum and dad are
I am thinking, thinking why aren't they here?
I am worrying, worrying they might have died
All I can hear are the sirens
And the hammering, hammering of my heart

I am five years old
I am sitting in the air raid shelter
I am shouting, shouting for Mum and Dad
I want them, want them here with me
I need them, need them to cuddle me
All I can hear are the sirens
And the hammering, hammering of my heart.

Lucy Foster (11)
Holmesdale Technology College, Snodland

WWII Worry

It was dark,
All I heard were screams from scared people,
I had lost my family; Mum, brother, sister,
I knew my dad was fighting.
As I ran to the shelter,
The air raid siren was ringing in my ears, over and over.
I looked back at the house,
It was tumbling down,
It had been hit,
And I wasn't sure if my family
Were caught in the rubble.
Once I got in the shelter,
I sat . . .
I sat alone.

Ember Bates (11)
Holmesdale Technology College, Snodland

91

World War I

World War I
Was the time the battle begun
The thought of dying
Others were crying.

Off went the guns
But there were no buns
You could see people dying
And dead people lying.

We put them to rest
In their very best vest
For when we win
We will make them pay for their sins.

Peace is all we ask for
But some people won't stop till they have won the war
See the glass on the floor
That's all of what is left from our door.

Daniella Barrett (13)
Holmesdale Technology College, Snodland

Libertine

I shy away from the norm
As others stay dormant.
I twist reality and make it my own
To kick the high men off their throne.
The seams they have sewn seem to never come undone
By those who sit back and watch the world go by.
I am a wild spirit, a person with my own views.
No one can catch me, put me in a jar and throw me on a shelf.
I am the every essence of me
No one can dilute
Or put me in a suit.
As the ribbon round my neck not only shows me
But the way I am free and able to see
The lies that the big man places.
So when others flee
I am the man standing on the mountain
Shouting 'Come and get me.'

John Jamie Simmons (16)
Holmesdale Technology College, Snodland

93

Untitled

Blue is the colour of variety
Blue can be dark, light or in the middle
Blue is the colour of a bright summer's day
Blue can be as light as a feather
But as dark as an evil witch's hat
Blue is peace, resting on the bank of a river
Resting at night, waiting for a wave to come
Blue can be anger, waiting to come out
But can be turned into the colours of a petal
Blue is not just a colour, it is a feeling
Bursting to come out, whatever the outcome
Who knows what it could be?
Because it is blue, nobody knows
Nobody knows what blue is
It is the sound of rest to some
But others don't know what blue is
Because it is blue, nobody knows
Will anybody find out what blue is
You never know, it might be you.

Ryan Sands (12)
Honywood Community Science School, Coggeshall

Bullies

Bullies, bullies, bullies
Calling me names.
Bullies, bullies, bullies
Calling me fat and ugly.
Bullies, bullies, bullies
I feel so alone.
Bullies, bullies, bullies
How can they be so mean?
Bullies, bullies, bullies
Why me?

Kim Thorpe (13)
Honywood Community Science School, Coggeshall

94

An Occasion

Tonight is the night
Don't go, stay tonight
Watching friends jigging and dancing
All of them to see, one last moment in time
Hip hop not jam, turn around

Tonight is the night
Don't go, shine tonight
Friends I see controlling music
And many I see dancing a duo.

And as we both, alone, take to the marble dance floor
The reverberating music slows
We begin our rhythmic dance
A sheen of mist clouds us from preying eyes.

When I found you
Violets bloomed
Nowhere I go.
Eyes close, a kiss of love
Is it not enough?
No one will surrender tonight
But I won't give in
I know what I want
And that's what I'll get.

But as she looks out at us
She feels jealousy, pain and anger
She unpins her hair
And starts plotting - revenge. . .

Luke Kyriacou (13)
Honywood Community Science School, Coggeshall

Destruction

Children crying,
Slowly dying.
Far from home,
All alone.

War wounds,
Lost tunes.
Dirty great trenches,
Near to benches.

Songs of sorrow,
Today and tomorrow,
Songs of praise,
Sung near to graves.

Bloody stains,
Come from gruesome veins.
Gruesome guns,
Damaged lungs.

Alone and shaking,
People awaking.
Dread and fear,
As dawn draws near.

Decimation,
As black as night.
All is lost,
What a terrible sight!

Lucy Argyle & Kayley Gymer (13)
Honywood Community Science School, Coggeshall

Not At All Bad

I'm in foster care,
At first I thought, *that's not fair!*
My friends get to stay with their mums and dads,
And I'm stuck here feeling so sad.
But it's not all bad!

My carers, they're the best,
In the beginning it was a test.
I broke their hearts,
And tore them apart.
The times were rough,
But they were tough!

At school was the worst task,
People began to ask,
'You're in care, *right?*'
I began to fight.
I felt they were mocking me,
But I would make them see!

But that past is no more,
Of that I am sure.
My foster mum and dad, my sister and I,
We see eye to eye.
I am no longer sad,
Because foster care is *not at all bad!*

Demi Morris (14)
Honywood Community Science School, Coggeshall

2 Minutes . . .

They fought . . .
In the unforgotten war . . .
They survived,
Or died,
And we get 2 minutes,
To remember
Them all.

Poppies . . .
They represent the war,
They grow in fields,
When it's the time of the war,

Wherever we are at 11 on the 11th November,
We stop,
We pause,
For 2 minutes . . .
Just 2 remember,
Just 2 remember,
Just 2 start,
Just 2 stop,
Just 2 die,
Just 2 cry,
Just 2 remember,
Just 2 remember . . .

Noamie Hull (13)
Honywood Community Science School, Coggeshall

Faith

Faith is all around us
Faith is being believed in
Faith can be colours
Faith can be words
Faith feels like you've just done something amazing
Faith makes you feel proud
Faith is everywhere.

Sean Bayes (13)
Honywood Community Science School, Coggeshall

98

That's War

The blood-stained people sitting in the trenches
Surrounded by maggots, rats and dead bodies as we're sitting
In the trenches
It's as black as night sitting in the trenches
And that's the trenches.

In the morning guns start firing
The guns as loud as a thousand drums
In the afternoon guns keep firing
Still as loud as a thousand drums
In the night guns stop firing until morning
Silence falls upon the fields at night

Screams and shouts all around
Obscene and open wounds all around
Blood and flesh splattered all around
And that's victims of war

Back at home air raids happen
They lay poppies for the dead
Back at home rations are happening
They live in hunger
Back at home they worry for the safety of the soldiers
They live in hope that their relatives return

And that's what war is all about!

George Bell (13)
Honywood Community Science School, Coggeshall

Blue . . .

Blue is the colour of a bright summer's day.
Blue is the colour of a blue sky on the summer's day.
Blue is the colour that sounds like birds tweeting.
Blue is the colour that smells like blossoming flowers.
Blue is the colour that tastes like blueberries.
Blue is the colour that feels like cotton wool, like puffy clouds.
Blue is the colour that lasts forever and ever.

Loren Clarke (12)
Honywood Community Science School, Coggeshall

99

Queen And Country

My hands are on the clutch,
I'm in control, yet sweating like a Christmas turkey.
Last time that came, I spent it with the love of my life.
Focus . . .
Bomb 1, drop!
The plane rustled as the explosion below pushed the sky to the moon
I'm blinded by the smoke in front
And deafened by the engines and screams of humans.
This is for Queen and country
This is revenge
Brutal, murderous revenge.
My job!
Bomb 2, drop!
The force makes us go into a barrel wheel roll.
They're surrounding us.
Shoot! We need more fuel.
Engine one gone!
Hold on tight man, we're going down
Coast!
We're gonna make it . . .
Engine 2 gone!

Lucy Pollard (13)
Honywood Community Science School, Coggeshall

When?

Why do they give lives?
Why do they take lives?
What do they do every day?
What are they doing today?
When will they come back?
When will they go off track?
This is
The army!

Adam Boulter (13)
Honywood Community Science School, Coggeshall

Remember!

Remember, remember the 11th of November
The people who died,
To save our lives
Remember, remember the 11th of November

Remember, remember the 11th of November
Our dad and grandads,
Who risked their lives to save our lives
Remember, remember the 11th of November

Remember, remember the 11th of November
Children crying,
Whilst dads were fighting
Remember, remember the 11th of November

Remember, remember the 11th of November
Blood-stained men,
Who are getting repaired
Remember, remember the 11th of November

Remember, remember the 11th of November
Men were tiring,
Whilst guns were firing
Remember, remember the 11th of November.

Grace Hayhoe (13)
Honywood Community Science School, Coggeshall

The Crying Cloud - Crying Pylvi

The clouds cried above the poppies,
But helping them in their growth.
Soldiers exchanging deathly shots,
Fighting for their country, where they swore their oath.
They came to a foreign shore,
Hoping to find a lot more.
In the trenches they lay, choking away
Hoping for safety, they pray

Thomas Doubleday (13) & Amir Berkane (14)
Honywood Community Science School, Coggeshall

101

The Field Of Death

Lonely and isolated,
alone in the field,
all in the dark,
with terror and fear.

Screaming can be heard
from miles around,
as sick people die under the ground,
trenches are filled with bodies and blood,
as yet for tomorrow has still not begun.

People crying, people dying,
all in spirit and fear,
souls are crying as death is coming,
for their sorrow and tears.

Fighting can be heard from miles around,
as people cry and people shout,
no one can hear as the bombs are loud,
so you're on your own till sundown!

Fern Blackburn & Lauren Lane (14)
Honywood Community Science School, Coggeshall

The Secret Within

We made love, it is our fate.
It was a little too late
The father is now no more
For he cannot take the floor
As the butterfly inside me awaits
For the world I have yet to create
As I took that daring step
Every day from then on, I wept.
As I go around the same
I will always feel that pain
I still see the image in my head
As my baby is now dead.

Natasha Wilson & Rebecca Brooker (14)
Honywood Community Science School, Coggeshall

1o2

Sport

Running like your life depended on it,
Everything around you is in slow motion.
Your coach is in your head, got to be fit, fit, fit!
The standing crowd making such a commotion.

The commentator's drone booming through the megaphone,
The track, like a red carpet stretched in front of you.
Whether you will win, it is not known!
Your head is weighing you down, what to do?

The breath on your neck from the runner behind,
Your tight-fit clothes trapping you in,
You know your body is almost resigned,
The thumping implanted in your brain, making you spin.

Your run is worth more than just gold,
You don't smile, just grin and bear it.
You're coming in first, don't get too bold,
Young runners out there, got to be fit, fit, fit!

Emma Napthine (14)
Honywood Community Science School, Coggeshall

The Shiver Of His Fear

The banging of a gun,
As he falls down on his knees,
The shiver of his fear,
Is beating down on me.

The cracking of his bones,
As they fall down to a halt,
The shiver of his fear,
Is beating down on me.

He falls down to his death,
I feel so very alone,
The shiver of his fear,
Is beating down on me.

Lucy Sykes (13)
Honywood Community Science School, Coggeshall

103

Air Raid

The siren sounds,
Children cry,
Hearts pound.
Alright, parents lie.

Loud as the sound of a thousand drums,
Bombs fall heavily on the town.
Planes and helicopters, they have come,
Buildings and houses all fall down.

All is dark,
All is calm.
Around the town people hark,
Nobody has come to any harm.

Except that little boy,
Who was always alone.
All he had, that one toy,
All he needed was a home.

Emily Rayner & Ashvi Chotai (13)
Honywood Community Science School, Coggeshall

The Ghost In Pain

I have never died before,
I am to live no more.
I am locked up in chains,
I am the ghost in pain.

I see you at my gravestone,
I have left you all alone.
It is driving me insane,
I am the ghost in pain.

I see you there, you start to cry,
I really did not mean to die.
I'm sorry I used to be so vain,
I am the ghost in pain.

But now something is happening to me,
It feels like I'm floating in the sea.
Not vain, no chains, no longer insane,
I am no longer the ghost in pain.

Emily Smith (13)
Honywood Community Science School, Coggeshall

The Prisoner

I could not see a thing,
A band around my eyes,
A matted cloth stuffed between my jaws,
My feet shuffled on the cold stone floor,

I thought of my family, if they were there
What would they think if they knew I was here?
Would they curse me under their breath
Or would they will for my death?

A sound of a whip brought me back
As it slashed five times across my broken back.
A cold steel pipe, pressed to my head,
One single shot and I was dead.

So here I am, a prisoner of war,
Here I lie, only a poppy to replace,
To replace the memory of our ill-gotten gains.

Josie Beaumont (13)
Honywood Community Science School, Coggeshall

Running Free

I was tearing through
The dense colour-washed horizon
A stream of blue
Came into view
The fiery sun shining down
On the luminous washed terrain.

I was still sprinting nobly
Then I had a recollection of thoughts
Memory after memory recovered
To my confused and undisputed intelligence

I was still running,
Through the background of
My sensitive thoughts.

Callum Norman (13)
Honywood Community Science School, Coggeshall

 106

I'm Not Asleep

When I'm 6-ft deep,
Do not weep,
I'm not there,
I'm not asleep.

It's not me lying, peaceful, quiet,
I've now escaped this world of riot.

I'll be up there,
Wherever 'there' is,
Happy smiling, no more crime,
No need to have a sense of time.

When I'm 6-ft deep,
Do not weep,
I'm not there,
I'm not asleep.

Kate Barham (14)
Honywood Community Science School, Coggeshall

Untitled

Come on, take it slow
I say three words that you already know
I love you mentally so it's time to show.
You mean too much for me to let you go
And for this song I'm going to show you my gentle side
We can leave our past behind
I had something but now I've got nothing to hide.
So when I feel I'm losing my brain
You are there to stop me going insane.
When I look at you I forget my pain.
You make life serious and not a game.
I would spend my life doing what you said for me to do
And I would end my life so no one ever gets to you.
I love you and there ain't no test.
You are my life, so life is the best.

Byron Gavin-Jones (14)
Honywood Community Science School, Coggeshall

107

Oh How I Miss Him

The way he left.
The way he broke my heart.
The pain he left me in.
The loneliness I felt every day and every night.

I will always remember the first time he met my parents.
The emotion on his face - so scared.
But I knew everything would be OK.
How I miss those days when he would come over to my house
and we would have a laugh and watch films.

The desperation to see his face one more time.
The desperation to see his smile, feel his soft touch.
To feel his heart beat one more time.
I would give my soul, even if it left me dark and cold.
Oh how I miss him!

Lauren Carpenter (14)
Honywood Community Science School, Coggeshall

Remembering Them

Sitting, scared and alone
Waiting and waiting until we go home.
People with bloodstained jackets.
Lying in the middle of blazing rackets.

Dancing and running away from the guns.
Faster and faster everyone runs.
Bloodshot faces
When everyone races.
Hearts being crushed
With a fast bullet rush.

So here I am lying
With ten other men,
With everyone saying,
'We will remember them.'

Eleanor Rutherford (14)
Honywood Community Science School, Coggeshall

Colour Poem

My favourite colour is blue
The colour of the sea and the colour of you

It reminds me of school
And the colour of water in a swimming pool

There are many types of this colour
Dark, light and even a flash of thunder

It is a touch of sadness
But as well, a bit of happiness

Blue has many special powers
It can climb Big Ben and many taller towers

My favourite colour is blue
The colour of the sea and the colour of you.

Mollie Foster-Gooding (12)
Honywood Community Science School, Coggeshall

SAS

A silent shot and a bullet shell drop,
A man lay still suffering in pain,
Another bullet shell dropped to the man again,
Shouting and cursing with last breaths,
Crawling to his medicine and using what was left,
Back up and clouds of dust appeared,
A perfect opportunity for the silent shooter to disappear,
A search went on, bangs and roars,
From army vehicle and enemy personnel and more,
Nothing found,
Nothing left only blood, terror and relief,
A big camo sheet was found next to three bullet shells,
Like the dead body, they lay still in a mess,
Deep down they all knew it was the work of the SAS.

Sonny Croydon (14)
Hugh Christie Technology College, Tonbridge

109

The Final Battle

He's been around the world
He's seen a million things
He's fought in countless wars
And dined with many beings
He's seen the Northern Lights
He's counted all the stars
Been inside and out Saturn's rings
And started life in heat.

He's fluent in life's languages
He's tasted each fayre
He's mingled with royalty
And lived what people dream
He was there when it began
And he knows when it will end
His only enemy was Man
And yet he was my dearest friend.

He began my evolution
Gave me my first breath
He was there at my reception
And my soul was with him in death.

Liam Sedeno (14)
Hugh Christie Technology College, Tonbridge

Childhood Memories

Going into my class
With the sun shining through the windows
Doing my work, waiting for the bell to get outside for break
As we sat there waiting for that bell . . .
Miss got her guitar out
And started singing
Everyone bored
Everyone sleeping
When will she let us leave?

George Bristow (14)
Hugh Christie Technology College, Tonbridge

110

Epic War

War is a terrible thing, there are lots of
dead bodies.
Crack! As the bullets travel as fast as an F1 car
across the battlefield.

Boom! As the car bomb goes off
and there's lots of smoke in the air.
Enemy helicopters are getting shot down
like flies.
We're shooting bullets at recognised faces.

Crack! As the bullets fly across no-man's-land.
I can hear the bullets coming across the battlefield
and I shout, 'Get down.'
All I can smell down in the trenches is the smell
of rotten boots.
Many of my fellow men are passing away.
Bang! The last man dies on the enemy's army.

Now this is the end of the epic war.

Stevie Cooksley-Buchanan (14)
Hugh Christie Technology College, Tonbridge

War Poem

The bombs fell and the people howled
The bangs were ever so loud
The fires got bigger as the forces got smaller
People fled as the tanks arrived

Time after time reinforcements were called
They never came and it started to get cold
One by one the men fell, just like dominoes

At last reinforcements, the tanks caught alight
And then there was a fair fight
As more soldiers arrived the opponent fled
We had won that small battle even though we were falsely led.

Ryan Hazelden (13)
Hugh Christie Technology College, Tonbridge

111

God's Hand

The noise of the mustard gas
people dying mass by mass
the field turned up by the boot print
democracy planning on a blueprint

Young soldiers dying, praying to the gods
as the head officer nods
more and more soldiers dying,
Germany tiring.

Soldiers marvel at the mayhem.
Enemy soldiers hating them.
A river of blood,
almost like a flood.

Adam Treharne (14)
Hugh Christie Technology College, Tonbridge

War Poem

Bullet shells are flying
People are dying
People begin to run
Killed by a team gun

When shots get fired
Confidence decreases
When the enemy gets killed
Confidence increases

People in tanks
People sniping from banks
The sun begins to rise
It's a new day.

Tyler Edwards (14)
Hugh Christie Technology College, Tonbridge

112

War Poem

A poppy represents the great big war,
A little red flower but there's more,
It's better than a story, it happened in real life,
They used metal guns and 10-inch knives.

Each soldier was someone really special,
They gave their lives for every living soul,
They may not be perfect,
But great fighters they were,
But most of them are gone now,
So remember them while *you* can!

Grace Shoebridge (14)
Hugh Christie Technology College, Tonbridge

Gallant Soldiers

Gallant soldiers shot their screaming guns at enemy foe
There was chaos as booming bombs crashed against friendly ground
Enemy guns boomed like stomping elephants at familiar faces.
Enraged enemy foes raced towards innocent men.

There was no place to go, no place to hide for amiable men
One by one fell and now they are memories
But they are loved and still loved for the things they've done.

Because they are the gallant soldiers.

Tom Broad (14)
Hugh Christie Technology College, Tonbridge

113

War Poem

The soldiers are brawling
Their bodies are falling
The soldiers had tried
Their families cried

A soldier fell asleep in a field
He woke up surrounded with no weapon to wield
The soldier had fear in his eyes
As I write this poem, another soldier dies.

Ryan Lower (14)
Hugh Christie Technology College, Tonbridge

My War Poem!

The lads marched, trudging like bedraggled zombies,
The hollow shells of once happy lads fought on without compassion.
Rats, lice and lack of rum,
No wonder some lads could no longer fight on.
The steady beat of long-forgotten uniform drills
Echoed vexingly inside their heads ever after.

Gemma Chatten (14)
Hugh Christie Technology College, Tonbridge

Dragon's Life

When they're born they are cute
Their cry is softer than a flute
From their birth, their wings are grown
Even though they have never flown
Their breath can't light a match
Although they can throw and catch
When they're older they get colder
Their breath can light a penholder
Their scales harden good and strong
But their nests really pong
As they grow big and proud
Their little chime gets really loud
Dragons' wings can now fly
They all could do it if they tried
Their eyes pierce into your soul
And force you to dig up coal
Dragons are as tough as nails
On their mountains they leave trails
As they age they go blind
In fact, their glory days are far behind
In their final days they have peace
Finally escaping life's cruel leash
This is a dragon's life, but it has a moral
All creatures have a life from us to bugs to coral.

Stevie Liennard (14)
Meadows School, Southborough

Love Is Like A Golden Chain

Love is like a golden chain
it binds two hearts together
and if you ever break that chain
you break my heart forever.

Love is like a feathered pillow
so soft, so warm and so tender
The more I feel, the more
I lie, the more I remember.

Your cute smile that always lasts a while
you always go that extra mile
the softness of your skin always has my heart aching
this is love in the making.

Cody Bryan (14)
Meadows School, Southborough

A Legend

And the stars guided
us that night
where our bodies
met like shore to sea,
and the lapping of the waves
were like kisses unto me.
Our fingers led by light of love
and those twinkles in your eye,
like stars falling upon us
from that passion-red sky.

And we were anchored
to the passing ships
as they drifted through,
our lips shimmering
as the waters washed us blue.
Turning skin to glistening scale
a legend we became,
washed upon the shore
a mythical love;
a modern folklore.

Aimée Williams (17)
Mid-Kent College, Chatham

Haiku

I can't see it yet
Oh no, hang on a minute
It's behind your ear.

Martha van Bakel (14)
Newstead Wood School for Girls, Orpington

117

Open Heart Surgery

Here, take my heart
You need it more than me
You'll benefit from it greatly
That's my guarantee

You can just cut me open
And take it from within
Just pass me that knife
And then we can begin

Firstly, watch what I do
Then you can do it too
Just below my heart
Push the knife through

OK, as you can see
The knife is now inside
Now take the knife off me
Then let it just slide

That's right, cut me deep
And let my blood ooze out
No, leave my blood dripping
I can do without

Next, make an incision
Right there, where I point
I need you to do this properly
So don't disappoint

Great, now can you see it
Beating away fast?
Just take that knife
And make that beat its last

Don't do it now,
Only when I say
OK, do it quickly
And make sure you don't delay

118

What are you waiting for?
Take out my heart
If my lungs are in the way
Just pull them apart

By the time I count to three
Make sure it is gone
Right, one . . . two . . . three
And then you are don-

Adedoja Opeymi Odunowo (17)
Newstead Wood School for Girls, Orpington

To Time And World Enough

Time flies
Light flies faster
Can disappear before time can
And never come back.

The dark isn't always the end.
It's never the end.
Born from the dark.
Born into the light.

Never enough time.
Never enough light.
But time still flies on.
Light even faster.

They'll never meet -
Flying separate journeys.
But time we can share.
Light we cannot.

Rachel Da Costa (16)
Newstead Wood School for Girls, Orpington

For You

I wish
For those who need my wishes

For those who need my prayers
I pray

I hear
For the deaf
The beautiful sounds
That no one should be deprived of.

I seek
For the blind
A heart's desire
That everyone has deep down.

I suffer
For the soldiers
Who need to be strong
To win endless wars.

I weep
For the angels
Who try so hard
To make the world a better place.

But

I dream
Only for myself.

Shayna Kowalczyk (12)
Newstead Wood School for Girls, Orpington

120

Used

Used.
Desolate.
Abandoned.
Alone.
Lying on the cold hard concrete, already come to the end
Of its life, ground into the dirt,
Into ash.

To be used
And then forgotten.
No thank you.
No future, its purpose complete.

It is almost impossible,
Unfeasible,
To imagine that once it was caressed
Between the warmth of two lips.

Every cloud has a silver lining,
Or so I'm told.
Fascinatingly, I am yet to see one for myself,
Or for this pour soul.

And we converse laugh, eat, sleep, strive and live,
And inhale foul vapours.
But what for? To end up like that lone cigarette butt?
To the end of life, ground into the dirt:

Alone?
Abandoned?
Desolate?
Used?
Really?

Not me.

Leodora Darlington (17)
Newstead Wood School for Girls, Orpington

121

The Perfect Picture

She was just a little girl
When her life was changed forever,
No older than eleven
She thought herself to be grown.
But then a tragic thing happened,
Her picture fell down.

Her parents were splitting,
How could this have ever happened?
Her family, she thought were perfect
Neither fights nor quarrels were seen or heard
Just her, her mum and dad.
The perfect picture indeed, you say.

But under the glaze, the paint was cracked
Gaping holes hidden from view.
Passers-by would never know
The problems this family faced
Or the pain the little girl would feel
For years and years to come.

She looks down at the painting,
Her pretty picture ripped in half.
Torn and destroyed and left to rot,
A tragic event indeed
But what is even more tragic
Is that little girl was me.

Fope Olaleye (13)
Newstead Wood School for Girls, Orpington

122

Kaleidoscope

I shake it, then listen to it, then cautiously peer
Through the glass hole. I am greeted by
Lemons, grapefruits,
Melons, leprechauns,
Dizzy daisies and drunken dots,
Swirling and dancing before my eyes.

They do not notice me much, but some beckon me forward -
Hypnotising me where I stand. Of course I want
To reach through the glass and join them,
But I am afraid that if I move an inch
They will disappear like a wonderful dream.

Then they start taunting me; laughing at my
Foolishness. They come closer to look at me,
The colours are nauseating. I can't breathe.
What is happening? Through the dizzying world
I see no happiness anymore - just cruel faces.

And as I begin to fall under the spell of these cruel,
Colourful and wild animals, I am jerked aside by my mother.
The kaleidoscope falls from my hands and as I bend down
To retrieve it, I see broken glass and jumping beads escaping;
I see a broken kaleidoscope containing my broken dreams.

Katie Russell (14)
Newstead Wood School for Girls, Orpington

Body Language

There are phrases that are echoed outside the spoken word.
Instead of lips forming words forming emotions emulating your
speech there is -
Silence.
Yet, what escapes from the arching of an eyebrow and the twisting
of a lip has more personality,
Than the blank language that the tongue moulds to take their form.
Such moulded phrases, like the pressing of clay are changeable
and meaningless.
If something can be so easily twisted then how can its interpretation
remain intact?
A thought when spoken can crumble and fade away.
On opening your mouth, not meaningful lyric but dust pours forth.
And you thirst to be known.
So speak, speak, and let yourself be heard. Not through the vocal
orations of vanity and form but from the joy of sharing without words.
Instead it is better to live by the silent expressions that reach out
and grasp, not the brain
But the soul.

Alix Penn (16)
Newstead Wood School for Girls, Orpington

124

Winter's White

In the morning's first light, it is glistening
Perfectly still, I'm listening
For the sounds of a white Sunday morn
Overnight, a new world has been born

Not a mark, nor a print nor a smear
On a layer so delicate, so sheer
Through an archway of white-topped trees
Bare and released of their leaves

The stillness and hush
Is replaced by the rush
And the laughter and joy
Of young girls and small boys

In the evening's first dark
On the street, in the park
Its dazzling white,
Cannot be enveloped by the night.

Toyo Adedoyin Odetunde (14)
Newstead Wood School for Girls, Orpington

125

Vertigo

It's a mosaic
Twisting
Colours shifting to
Blue
Red
Purple . . .
Then this craving entwined with the flood of butterflies in my gut
Sets the world whirling like a spinning top.
All I need is that sound,
That music
And your deep gaze boring into my soul
To release the cap -
Uncaged and euphoric
- Sets me pirouetting off the map

But when I fall I know your arms will catch me.

Bethany Wickramasighe (17)
Newstead Wood School for Girls, Orpington

Broken In Two . . .

I said I really loved you,
But you broke my heart in two
I said I was fine, I lied
What else was I supposed to do?

To me, I said you meant nothing
But inside I was the one suffering
I thought I trusted you . . .
But you were the one who broke me in
Two

I knew we weren't going to last long
Because so many things went wrong
So I had to pick a song to play
To remind me of you every day
When you were gone . . .

Gursharan Virk (13)
Northfleet School for Girls, Northfleet

126

The Life Of A Teenage Girl

I wake up in the morning,
With a really dizzy head,
The normal problems of a teenage child,
Who won't get out of bed,

My parents go through hell with me,
Because my moods are really black,
They don't know how to deal with me,
I'm a weight upon their backs,

The morning starts badly,
My uniform's a state,
Mum shouts up from down below,
'Come on you're going to be late!'

As I blunder down the stairs,
Shoving on my shoes,
I see the paper on the steps,
And gasp when I see the news.

The headline says that the school has gone,
Because of a demolition team,
Oh no, it's not, I'm still asleep,
It turns out it's a dream,

Up I jump, with a start,
I really am quite late!
I'm going to have to run not walk,
If I'm going to reach the school gate,

I run downstairs and slam the door,
Leaving the house in a whirl,
Another day begins again,
In the life of a teenage girl.

Laura White (13)
Northfleet School for Girls, Northfleet

127

The Best Christmas Present Ever

We waited for them to come out,
They never did,
They stayed back in the shadows
Really well hid.

We couldn't see them
So we lifted up the roof
Cuddled up together
We needed no more proof

We tried to hold them
But it took forever
They ran and ran around the cage
Closely squashed together

Eventually we caught them
We sat down on the floor
I stroked her gently
With my back against the door

Slightly shivering with the occasional flick
Ignoring the food waved by her nose
Soon she got comfortable
Her confidence grows

Then we heard a crunch
The other started eating
She sat still
I could feel her heart beating

The pounding changed to a rhythmic purr
Her fur puffed up big
She was the best Christmas present ever
My guinea pig.

Katie Kay (13)
Northfleet School for Girls, Northfleet

128

Music

In a recording studio,
There lived musical notes,
There was Rap, Modern and Rock,
Classical who did, well . . . not a lot.

One night when the moon was high,
The notes began to fight,
Rap turned to Rock and flashed his bling,
Rock pulled out a mike and started to sing.

Modern punches Classical around the face as hard as he can,
Classical falls to the ground and begins to cry out in pain,
Rock helps Classical up as Modern sings, 'Everybody In Love',
But suddenly Rap jumps upon Modern's back and starts
to attack from above.
Modern is left reeling in self pity as Rap starts to sing 'In The Ayer',
Everyone whines at the top of their voices, that's all but Classical,
Classical leaves the other notes to fight out an endless battle
over who's better,
So she decides to write and send a helpful letter.

The next night there was a visitor who came just before the fight,
The notes were left gasping at the sight,
Pop had come to show who was top,
But also to show the others how much their singing 'flops'!

She began to sing 'Rockin' Robin',
And much to her amazement the others bowed down and cheered,
For she was the queen and they were her subjects,
So there was never the petty fight ever again!

Rebecca Morris (13)
Northfleet School for Girls, Northfleet

It's Not All About Me!

I am nearly a teenager.
I am all the things of my past
And soon to be my future.
I am the life of my mother
And the nose of my father.
I am the sun rising,
The waves crashing,
And the birds singing.
I can be whatever I want to be.
I want to be me, I want to
Walk the streets with a bottle of Coke
In my purple wellies and orange raincoat,
Kicking stones along the pavement,
Spending all my money on make-up -
That's the wrong shade for me;
Me, the li'l' old milk bottle with my pal Shelby
Who usual talks me out of (or encourages me into)
My stupid ideas.

It's not all about me, or anyone else.
Of course I have issues.
But so does the next person,
Who is as equal to me and anyone else.
But not the same as me or anyone else.
I don't want to be anything,
I want to be me.

Rachel Johnson (12)
Northfleet School for Girls, Northfleet

130

Beneath Your Feet

You watch the waves rise and fall
Your board is in your other hand
Standing there smiling and tall
Your board will be your best tool

You laugh
You cry
You sing
You dance
You fight
You scream
You joke
You jump
You run!

Towards the waves
The sky is blue
The surf is good
Your timing is right

And you surf the waves
Your board beneath your feet
You prepare your next stunt
In this game you cannot cheat.

Ellesha Ryan (13)
Northfleet School for Girls, Northfleet

Rainbow

Red is for roses, red is for love.
Yellow is for sunshine, it comes from above.
Pink is for pretty on a spring day.
Green is for grass, let's go outside and play.
Purple is for grapes, they ripen in the sun.
Orange is for orange, why don't you try one?
Blue is for beautiful, blue is for sky.
White is for clouds way up high.

Samantha Hurdle (12)
Northfleet School for Girls, Northfleet

Single Rose

Waiting, waiting, waiting,
No sign at all.
Waiting, waiting, waiting,
And my single rose falls.

Tears trickle from my eyes,
Looking down at the muddy ground.
While I think of all those lies,
That I have found.

Waiting, waiting, waiting,
No sign at all.
Waiting, waiting, waiting,
And my single rose falls.

Why is he still not here?
I thought I loved him so much more.
Hopefully he should be near,
Because my heart is so sore.

Waiting, waiting, waiting,
No sign at all.
Waiting, waiting, waiting,
And my single rose falls.

Chloe Wallaker (12)
Northfleet School for Girls, Northfleet

Try, Try, Try Again

I'm trying to write a poem,
A poem I'm trying to write,
There is no explanation for my lack of inspiration,
Words just will not come to me,
However hard I try,
I cannot find my rhythm,
I cannot find a rhyme,
Come back imagination . . .
Then I'll try another time.

Katie Ryan (13)
Northfleet School for Girls, Northfleet

132

Dreams

Every night I go to sleep,
Quick, without a peep.

And every night I have a dream,
It's always a different theme.

On Monday I was under the sea,
Drinking cups of tea.

On Tuesday I went into space,
Just discovered an alien race.

On Wednesday I went back in time,
It cost a lot more than a dime.

On Thursday I went to Niagara Falls,
Bounced around some basketballs.

On Friday I went back to school,
I did maths, how uncool.

On Saturday I got a lolly,
I got it off a girl called Molly.

On Sunday I lay in the sun,
Munching on a nice iced bun.

Sophie Watson (12)
Northfleet School for Girls, Northfleet

Edward Barry

Oh dearest Edward Barry,
Why'd you have to go?
Because Edward Barry, I miss you so.

Your smile, your laugh,
Your strange hate of baths,
Your tears, your frown,
You never let me down.

RIP Edward Barry.

Alice Glisson (12)
Northfleet School for Girls, Northfleet

133

The Dream

I close my tired eyes; I drift deep into thought,
I dream that I am in a judicial court.
With people staring - eyes all around,
Why am I here? Why am I surrounded by a crowd?
I hear gasps and raised voices, and people throwing the blame,
I feel centre of attention, but I feel so alone - am I sane?
The judge glares at me, I feel so afraid,
I haven't done anything bad - I feel so betrayed.
I step outside for a breath of fresh air,
You're not meant to step out of trial but I don't care.
I feel dizzy, faint and extremely ill,
I fall to the ground - staying dead still.
My eyes are firmly shut; do I want to see the light?
I get up onto my knees, and am afraid of the sight.
I'm in my lounge, right back to where I was before,
What had happened? Why was I sitting on the floor?
I will never quite know what happened that day.
But you do know what people say:
Everything that is, or was, began with a dream.

Giorgia Antoncini (13)
Northfleet School for Girls, Northfleet

Fingers, Thumbs And Toes

My finger is longer than my thumb,
My thumb is bigger than my toe,
My toe, don't you know,
Is warm in my sock,
My finger on the other hand,
Is in my glove.
My glove you know,
Isn't just for show,
And neither is my toe,
My glove keeps me warm,
And my toe helps me walk.

Jaspreet Kaur Kooner (13)
Northfleet School for Girls, Northfleet

134

Who Would I Be?

Who would I be,
If I walked in the sand
And ran in the sea,
Touched the moon and
Jumped on a tree?

Who would I be
If I had three toes and one ear,
Right-handed
Left-handed
With nothing to fear?

Who would I be,
If I squealed like a mouse,
And roared like a lion,
Ran like a zebra
And swam like a hippo?

Who would I be?
Definitely not me!

Emma Bannister (13)
Northfleet School for Girls, Northfleet

Word

Please! Please!
Let me out!
Don't make me scream and shout!
Just let me be seen!
Why are you so mean?
I'm just one little word
In one big book
Would it hurt if they had a look?
I'm sorry I didn't mean to call you big
But you have to admit, you're a bit of a pig
A pig for words, silly!
Do you really think I would be that mean? Really?

Connie Burr (12)
Northfleet School for Girls, Northfleet

135

In My Memory

In my memory
I remember you,
I can picture your eyes,
And your wide open smile,
Your long, long legs,
You could run a mile.

In my memory,
I can see your long fingers,
You'd paint them every day
With a bright pink nail varnish,
Which looked good in its own way.

In my memory I can see your whole body,
Your slim, streamline figure.
I was always jealous.

In my memory,
I remember you,
My best friend.

Emilie Lock (12)
Northfleet School for Girls, Northfleet

Holidays

We go on holiday nearly every year,
Sometimes it can be a bit dear,
We go to Cyprus, Bulgaria or even Spain,
But I hate it when I have to travel by plane,
Whenever we come back I usually look quite tanned,
Unless I go somewhere cold then I look rather bland,
I can't always understand what people say,
So I'll usually just walk away,
The food can also be very alarming,
But I suppose some boys can be quite charming,
It's always good if there's a water ride,
And always put suntan lotion on or you'll get fried.

Jodie Butcher (13)
Northfleet School for Girls, Northfleet

136

Who Am I?

Am I someone who makes people feel good about themselves
When I don't?
Am I someone who blocks everyone out of my life?
Do I feel good about who I am?
Am I the selfish one who only cares about themselves?
Who am I?

I want to be a person who is cheerful all the time,
I want to be someone who cares for others, other than themselves,
I want to be the kind of person that goes with what feels right,
To try and be an individual,
Not trying to be someone I'm not,
Am I one of those people?

Am I selfish?
Unkind?
Happy?
Caring?
So who am I?

Monica Helaith (12)
Northfleet School for Girls, Northfleet

A Snowy Day

As the segments of a snowflake delicately swoop
onto the tip of my nose,
I watch the children build a small snowman,
shaping it in a certain pose.
Spiderwebs look like lace shimmering when the sun
can seep through the clouds up above.
The houses covered in a blanket of white,
everyone snug inside, full of love.
A cold day outside is grabbed and taken away
by a hot roast dinner.
A cold night inside is taken away by a hot water bottle
tucked under your duvet ready for you.
A snowy day tends to be a nice day.

Eleaner Hardy (13)
Northfleet School for Girls, Northfleet

137

My Dinosaur Fred!

I was thinking last night
Whilst lying in bed
What if I had a dinosaur
Named Fred.

He'd be green
And he'd be tall
But he might not be
So beautiful

He'd be my hero
He'd be my mate
I could stay up with him
Until really late

Now I'm asleep
Lying in bed
Awaiting a dream
Of my dinosaur named Fred.

Lacey Deighton (13)
Northfleet School for Girls, Northfleet

Lucky

Cute brown eyes,
Black floppy ears,
When I first saw him I burst into tears,
Not because of sadness but because of joy,
I will love him forever,
My baby boy.

Katie Humphreys (13)
Northfleet School for Girls, Northfleet

Bullying

When I go to school,
I keep my head down,
I try to hide,
In case the bully's around.

Every day in class,
I feel neglected,
Even through break,
I get rejected.

When school ends,
I run to the gates,
I avoid the park,
That's where the bully waits.

Who shall I tell?
Who will be there?
If I were to die,
It would end this nightmare.

Asha Bhaker (12)
Northfleet School for Girls, Northfleet

Sweeties

Strawberry laces fizzing on my tongue
Chocolate truffles wow, they're yum!
Flying saucers exploring my tum
Smarties jumping one by one
Cola bottles having lots of fun
Bonbons rolling, who will win at the end run?
Hubba Bubba blowing bubbles
Marshmallows melting together in doubles
Toxic Waste causing trouble
Many of these are loveable
But take a good look inside and they are horrible.

Nikita Dhillon (12)
Northfleet School for Girls, Northfleet

139

The Missing Piece

I'm like the puzzle you never got to finish
Waiting for the last piece to be placed in
When you don't know what slot I fit into.
I go straight into the bin!

After all the misplacing
I just won't fit into my place
You are just too slow to build me up
So you will have to get with the pace!

You've tried your best to build me up
But you just can't seem to get it right
So now you'll probably put me away
Right out of your sight and ready to use another day!

I'm in my box all packed away
Ready to be put together
If you find the missing piece
You'll remember the picture on me forever!

Ekim Erbas (13)
Northfleet School for Girls, Northfleet

What Is Pink?
(Based on 'What is Pink?' by Christina Rossetti)

What is pink? A heart is pink, thumping inside me
What is red? A devil's red, with its sharp horns
What is green? Well fields are green, with their grass and leaves
What is blue? Of course my eyes are blue, like the river flowing
What is black? Why blackbirds are black and the blackboard
What is gold? Why gold is gold, like corn in the fields
What is white? A piece of paper is white, which you draw on
What is yellow? Well daisies are yellow, the colour of buttercups.

Evie Russell (13)
Northfleet School for Girls, Northfleet

Thank You

Thank you for everything
Everything past and been
For staying with me through times
When lots of friendships died

For times I wasn't so sure
You got me to the cure
Of all the problems that started
All the problems that parted

I know I don't say it often enough
And I know times have been tough
So I'm taking this chance to say
Thank you, and if I could . . .

I'd thank you every day!

Rebecca Longman (13)
Northfleet School for Girls, Northfleet

Memories

Memories, good and bad
Memories, happy and sad
Memories, any time of the day
Memories, home and away
Memories in black and white
Memories that give you a fright
Your memories, relive your dreams
Memories for you and me.

Leigh-Ann Freelove (12)
Northfleet School for Girls, Northfleet

Circus

Jumping lights,
Horses wild,
The air is cold,
Yet I feel mild.

> Clowns on skates,
> Magician magic,
> I watch a race,
> I'm a circus addict.

Anticipation builds
As the fireworks start
The exact memory
Will forever remain in my heart.

Jessica Silver (13)
Northfleet School for Girls, Northfleet

My Pencil

My pencil writes,
My pencil draws,
My pencil snaps when shut in doors,
In the grip of my hand.
We work as a team
To get the work done,
So easily!

Abbie Howard (13)
Northfleet School for Girls, Northfleet

142

My Rubber

My rubber erases the things that I do,
It gets rid of my mistakes and doodles too,
It's fat and it's white,
It's white and it's fat,
It's really rather tall,
It gets rid of mistakes,
It gets rid of them all.

Hannah-Marie Gillespie (12)
Northfleet School for Girls, Northfleet

Friends

F riends forever, we will be,
R andom people we shall see,
I like my friends the way they are,
E ncouragement will take us far,
N ever-ending respect for all,
D azzling laughter fun and full,
S upporting each other for evermore.

Nissern Bessioua (13)
Northfleet School for Girls, Northfleet

143

The Crackling Death Of Oliver Bran

Oliver Bran
Oliver Bran
Stuck his head in a frying pan

Frying pan
Frying pan
In and out Oliver Bran

Oliver Bran
Oliver Bran
Went sizzle, sizzle, crack, bang!

Crack, bang
Crack, bang
Went the face of Oliver Bran

Oliver Bran
Oliver Bran
Fried away in a crackling pan

Crackling pan
Crackling pan
Burned the last hair of Oliver Bran

Oliver Bran
Oliver Bran
Turned into a panther man

Panther man
Panther man
Finally died from a frying pan.

Mathumy Ratnavel (13)
Oaks Park High School, Ilford

144

I'm Invisible

I stare at you every day
but yet I'm invisible
I talk to you as my heart beats fast
but yet I'm invisible
I ask you out, you said no
then I'm invisible again
I tried, I tried, love has failed
I won't try, I won't try
stop searching for love
Love don't know me
I don't know love too
but yet I'll be invisible
I dream of you
but yet I wonder if I'll be with you
I am invisible to love
but yet love finds others
I close my eyes, you are there
I open them and smile
I'm still invisible to love
Maybe I'm ugly, maybe I'm fat
maybe I'm ginger, but that's that
but yet I'm invisible to love
Love finding is true
I won't give up
neither should you
even if I'm invisible to love
Love can find you
if you stay true
Live in peace and be you
because someone will love you for you.

Cerrina Ball (14)
Ormiston Park Academy, Aveley

Deserve

I deserve to be punished for the things I say
I deserve to be lonely for the heartache that strays
I deserve pain and nothing good
I deserve to be normal and happy.

I deserve to have a normal life and a happy future
Not pain and corrosive heartache
All the days pass like a flaming fire
Hitting every glass window that surrounds
My happiness, sometimes I wish I could
See the spraying sparkling water which sprays
My hot steaming fire out.

But it's like a black tunnel without any light
Surrounding my life I only see darkness and fear which sucks all the happiness out of me.

I deserve love and care
I deserve to be me and not be afraid to show it
I deserve to see that sparkling shimmering light
I deserve everything, but the only thing I don't deserve is another bad memory flooding my tears.
I deserve to see the swallowing birds that fly above the blue crystal sea reflecting off the shimmering scorching sun.

I deserve to have no pain, but life is unfair and cruel, it possesses the most poisonous substance
It's not the grey polluted world we live in but the life we lead
Maybe one day I will see how life always takes the good and never looks into a bad person's eyes.
For what is a world without any good people, it will bring fear, loneliness and pain
Which will always sway through the whistling shimmering wind letting off tiny sparkles every time it hits a tree.

I deserve to live my life through another's eyes and one day see the
true me
But for now I live in a world where I'm trapped and scared.

I deserve to be free and see the wildflowers which shimmer
graciously through the motioned wind
But most of all I want to be me.

Leanne Drain (15)
Ormiston Park Academy, Aveley

Best Friends

A friend is there
From start to end
Far or near
Here to mend
A true friend
Will be there
From every hug to every tear
Always share
Never disappear
For a click of the finger
And they appear

To mend your broken heart
And bring a smile to your face
They will never be too far away
A best friend for me is . . .

Grace Leeman is kind-hearted and there to cheer you up
Tino Karase is smart and a lovely friend to be around
Alanta Lawless is funny and thoughtful of others
Yasemin Acikel is funny and smart
Casey Mclean is weird (in a good way) and hilarious
And Robert Field, well you gotta love him
I love you guys.

Toni Adebajo (11)
Ormiston Park Academy, Aveley

147

My Mum

Me and my family sit on a hill in Scotland,
It's not just a hill,
It's my mum's favourite hill,
Before she passed away,
We always said that we will go there,
So some day I will go,
With my family,
Just sitting there on the hill,
As the hot sunshine lights up the sky,
As we sit in the sun,
My mum will be watching us all,
We all will play and eat together,
We all will go there each year to remember her,
Remember her kindness,
Her smile on her face,
Remember her,
We sit there all day long,
We just sit there,
Sit there thinking about her,
On her favourite hill.

Caitlin Rice (12)
Ormiston Park Academy, Aveley

Dream

Morning and the sun awakes in a beautiful place
called South Africa.
With outstanding animals prancing about
and trees gleaming in the sun.
As the sunsets the fire starts and the people dance.
The sea twinkles in the moonlight as the lions go to sleep.
I would love to go see the waves twinkling in the moonlight
as I sit on the beach.
And as the heat is still beaming I lay back
and look at the diamond stars in the blue velvet sky.

Lauren Ward (13)
Ormiston Park Academy, Aveley

148

Tokyo

I wake up to the sound of traffic and people talking as they walk by.
Giant buildings as tall as an old oak tree.
Automatic doors opening and closing constantly.
Tourists lost in the hectic city.
A Japanese flag flickers past the window.
The smell of sensational sushi and stringy noodles wafts past my room.
A view of the Imperial Palace starts off my day.
Its beautiful moat surrounds the palace.
Its old trees protecting it from any unwanted tourists.
As I look further along I see flash posters advertising new, more advanced technology.
Business men and woman walking past paying no attention to the road or path but more attention to their phone call.
Young children mucking around, causing distress to their parents, much to the amusement of the people walking past.
The day comes to an end.
The buildings and street lights come to life.
I lie down knowing that tomorrow will be the same.

Tiffie Ruane (13)
Ormiston Park Academy, Aveley

She . . .

She's a mermaid fresh from the sea,
She's as graceful as a bee.

She's a raging spark of fire,
She's an unwritten book
And when she speaks words that have died
They spring to life.

Her words are beautifully shaped,
No matter how small
And behind each word,
Behind each word,
There's an emotion too great to tell.

Tino Karase (12)
Ormiston Park Academy, Aveley

149

My Dog Ruby

I've got a little Staffie
She's black and white
She loves Rich Tea biscuits
And lays on my bed at night.

She wakes me in the morning jumping on my bed
She digs her little claws in and sits on my head.

She is very naughty
She pulls washing off the line
She drags it around the garden
But I love her cos she's mine.

She digs holes in the garden
And scratches at the door
She loves to chase her tail around
And puts mud on the floor.

Every day when I'm at school
She sits by the door to wait for me to come home again
Cos I am her best mate.

Billy Jeeves (11)
Ormiston Park Academy, Aveley

Eagle

I was at my house
When I heard a noise,
I went outside
And I saw an eagle
With wide brown wings
And big brown eyes,
It stared at my face
In a way I can't explain,
So I went closer,
He lay down,
I jumped on him
And we flew away . . .

Ewelina Glebinska (12)
Ormiston Park Academy, Aveley

150

When The Clowns Come To Town

When the clowns come to town,
All the children change their frowns,
And the mice tap their feet,
To the rhythm and the beat,
But the grannies think of woes,
Then all the grandchildren moan.

When the clowns come to town,
All the children can think of is wow,
And the teacher says, 'Think of better words,'
But the children shouting, 'We don't wanna be nerds!'

When the clown comes to town,
All the children change their frowns,
And the mice tap their feet,
To the rhythm and the beat,
But the grannies think of woes,
Then all the grandchildren moan.

So that's what happens when the clowns come to town.

Paul Chintua-Chigbu (11)
Ormiston Park Academy, Aveley

Why Friends Are Friends

Friends are friends
They are always right beside you
They will always be there
Right in front of you
When you need them most or not at all
They will be there if you give them a call.

Friends are like flowers
So lovely and sweet
They will like you even better
If you give them a treat
But if you don't they will not mind
Because friends are the loving kind.

Hayley Vincent (11)
Ormiston Park Academy, Aveley

151

My Wishes

Mighty force of Mother Earth
Here, we flowers
See our Earth
Might force of Father Sky
Hear our whisper, heed our cry
Gathered here stand your flowers
Who breathe the air and touch the land
United as seekers in this hour to summon forth mighty power
Forces of nature, darkness and light
Aid your seekers on this night
By earth, air, fire and water
Grant us each our heart's desire in this rightful ready hour
We call upon the ancient power
Grant us each what has been sought
Create reality from humble thought
On this night with harm to none
By our will it shall be done
So make it be.

Rishon Atkins (12)
Ormiston Park Academy, Aveley

Snowtime Fun

I know a place
Snowy and soft
When I wake
Cold but happy

White and fun
Playing and running
Bright and sunny
When I play it's funny

Snowboarding and skiing
For all the people staying
Swimming is fun
Now I am done.

Sasha Seddon (12)
Ormiston Park Academy, Aveley

152

The Beast!

There is a beast
Who sleeps all day
Waiting for his feast
He never comes out in May.

Clapping his dangerous sharp teeth
Licking his huge red lips
Whilst flies by a leaf
Its dinner time he sips.

The beast jumps up from his danger bed
Sharpens his deadly claws
And hides his massive furry brown head
Whilst his victims fall to the floor.

The stomach rumbles
His victim screams
The thunder crumbles
Then silence it beams.

Grace Leeman (12)
Ormiston Park Academy, Aveley

Paris

When I wake up I want to hear busy streets,
I want to be there for weeks and weeks,
Trying the different foods, hoping they are fresh and new.
The sounds of cars beeping their horns,
Rushing through the traffic-trapped roads.
This is the only place I want to be.
To see the waking lights during the night keeping us safe,
Just lighting up the whole of the city like sparkling diamonds in a
velvet-blue sky.
The loud music and busy bars,
I want these to make me feel free and alive.
Paris is where I want to live
And one day I will make it come true.

Kara Cross (12)
Ormiston Park Academy, Aveley

153

Wind

Fighting against you
Whispering in your ear
You're trying to get home
But you are nowhere near

> You try to fight him off
> But he always comes back
> When you do find shelter
> He fits through a crack

Wherever you walk
He follows you around
You feel like he's stalking you
But he doesn't make a sound

> You want to get rid of him
> But when you do
> He wails and he wails
> He is waiting for you.

Munro Ross (13)
Ormiston Park Academy, Aveley

Be Proud Of Your Face!

I'm very happy at what my face looks like,
It's the best part of me.
It laughs, it cries and sometimes smiles,
But my face is the best part of me.

Sometimes it shows some horrible signs
And maybe some good ones too,
But I'm proud of my face,
Are you?

Some people have spots and freckles,
But what's wrong with that? They're special.
Be proud of your face,
It's the best part of you!

Vicky Brown (11)
Ormiston Park Academy, Aveley

154

Snow

The glittery snowflakes drift gently down to the ground,
Like a lace curtain,
Gleaming and proud.

The snowflakes suddenly settle,
Making the ground a white carpet,
Whilst the adults put on the kettle.

The children race outside,
To build the biggest snowman,
Their faces streaked with a smile of pride.

The snow gradually disappears as the children play,
Even with only a thin layer left,
They still decide to stay.

Then they walk back inside as the sun shows its face,
Melting the snow,
No longer a magical place.

Anna Venemore (11)
Ormiston Park Academy, Aveley

The Greatest Nan

My nan used to make me laugh all the time
We would just keep laughing
Every minute, every day
She drove her granny-mobile
Making people laugh at her
Everyone thought she was the world's greatest

Losing my nan was the worst thing in my life
And it took me a long while to pick myself up
Happy, upset or angry, I won't forget my nan
Greatest lady in the world
Hope I don't forget her
I love you always and you are always in my heart.

Ryan Barry (13)
Ormiston Park Academy, Aveley

155

My Dog Sadie

I've got a dog called Sadie
She is fat and lazy
She is black and ginger
And is feisty as a ninja

She is two years old
Brave and bold
She likes her food
And to me she's very rude

She can be as humble as a bee
Her eyes are as blue as the sea
She likes the garden
Also she can't say pardon

I love my dog
And she loves me too
I know it.

Jack Fry (11)
Ormiston Park Academy, Aveley

My Two Gerbils

My two gerbils,
One is called Snowy,
She is as white as shepherd's delight,
Snowy is lazy and might be asleep
As she spends all her days in a craze
She chews wood which does not do any good.

My other gerbil is called Ginger,
She is so crazy,
She goes bonkers and eats lots,
When trying to catch them,
It is hard because they are
Very fast!

Carmen Byford (11)
Ormiston Park Academy, Aveley

156

Earth

Recycle with your peers
All the paper, card and glass
Bash the cans, trash the tins

Whenever I go to school
Here's my golden rule
Use my feet, take a bike
Take a bus, and no cars

Snow falls like a wolf barking
Once settled it's a peaceful puppy
Laying lazily to be played with.

Our environment is a changing
Things are dying and burning
Money is going - it's called the recession
Make this world a peaceful one
For a better future.

Chantel Nyamesre (11)
Ormiston Park Academy, Aveley

Untitled

I know a place
Where I can enjoy
Bright yellow sand
With palm trees stuck on the land

Markets in the distance
Sailing out to share
See the astonishing view

Me and ice cream
Lying together on the beach
Can't let go
It's a beautiful place.

Jake Riley (13)
Ormiston Park Academy, Aveley

157

Spain

If I could go anywhere I would go to Spain
Lovely hot sun
Have a lovely tasty bun
You won't need any socks
Don't forget your sunblock
Also don't forget your flippy floppy flip-flops
Have a dip in the pool
The pool is as blue as a dolphin
A trip to the spa
Why not go to the bar?
Relax in the hotel room
The sun is in bloom
The sun is bright
It is really light
Spain is really enjoyable fun and cool country
I would love to go to Spain!

Michaela Byford (13)
Ormiston Park Academy, Aveley

England

If I could be anywhere I would be England
On a Sunday morning
With my friends
Playing football to win the game
Being a captain brings responsibility
Leading my team to victory.

The pitch is muddy
It's also a bit sludgy
But I don't care
I will travel anywhere.

England is the place for me
And I want to see
All the sights for miles
Waiting for me.

Ben Smith (12)
Ormiston Park Academy, Aveley

Stuck In School

This is so boring
I am snoring

I wish I was in bed
But instead
I'm stuck 'ere
With no cheer

The stupid teacher
I could teach her
A few lessons in English
Cos she speaks gibberish

I feel like I'm in a zoo
Cos I'm stuck like glue
Without a clue
What, what should I do?

Emma Barrow (12)
Ormiston Park Academy, Aveley

Dogs

Big dogs
Small dogs
Fat dogs

Everyone loves dogs
But not so much as frogs
Dogs are funny
But cost lots of money

Black dogs
White dogs
Spotty dogs

There are so many dogs to choose
You just cannot lose
They bring lots of joy
But are never a toy.

Danielle Brewer (11)
Ormiston Park Academy, Aveley

159

A Girl's Fairy Tale

A girl's fairy tale is to be at a ball
And when the clock ticks it will be time to go
You lose a shoe but no need to fear
Because the prince that you danced with brings it back to you
The story goes on
You live life well
But not everything can be happy in a fairy tale
The two ugly sisters will spoil your fun
When your happy fairy tale has just begun
You will lose your way and you will have nowhere to go
You look through the tunnel
And think, when will the light show?
You will blame yourself
And your heart will grow heavier
And I am sorry, that is the way the fairy tale goes.

Gracie-Jay Nixon (12)
Ormiston Park Academy, Aveley

Skateboarding

S kating on their skateboards
K ids playing in the street
A nd trying new tricks
T he wind through their hair
E veryone having fun
B ouncing over things
O ver hills
A nd skating away
R adical dudes
D odging all the people
S kating up and down.

Leigh O'Donoghue (12)
Ormiston Park Academy, Aveley

Tails

Tails the flying fox
His friend is Sonic
He has two tails
His enemy is Robotnick
Or Robotnick's nickname is Eggman
He flies around all day
With his friends
Then he has a break (food)
Then he gets back to business
And destroying the spy monkeys
Tails' real name is Miles Tails.

Jonathan Madle (11)
Ormiston Park Academy, Aveley

Hawaii

Music playing, joyful dancing, I begin hula dancing.
I dream about Hawaii once again.
My hula skirt sways like a palm tree in a Hawaiian breeze.
The pineapple punch as sweet and fresh as can be.
The shiny golden sun shines down on my beautiful blonde hair.
We have our yummy traditional Hawaiian food but just then . . .
Boom!
Awoken by a noisy London morning.
Not a sight of Hawaii, nor smell, nor taste, nor picture, my world is gone,
My world is gone.

Shannon Lougheed (13)
Ormiston Park Academy, Aveley

161

The Caribbean Beach And Me!

The sand is as soft as a rose petal,
The waves crash against the shore,
Birds singing to the rhythm of the wonderful wind,
The sun is as hot as the lava that comes out a volcano,
The sea is as clear as the crystals,
The sky is as blue as the Pacific Ocean,
Drinks as tropical as the Caribbean itself,
And the food as fresh as a just made cake,
Not forgetting the magnificent sunset
And the fresh breeze that hits me in my face.

Nikeida Gerald (13)
Ormiston Park Academy, Aveley

Poppy, My Lovely Horse

Over the fields and far away,
My pony and I go out for a lovely ride,
Poppy's a New Forest pony and I love her lots,
She's full of fun and she's very kind,
She tosses her head and waves her tail around,
I hope our friendship lasts forever and never ends,
I love her lots and she loves me lots and we are in harmony,
Over the fields and far away,
My pony and I go out to play,
Love you Poppy.

Chelsea Bowen (11)
Ormiston Park Academy, Aveley

My Africa

My Africa is sunny and bright
We go on safari in the jungle in my jeep
Animals everywhere here in the wild
What a great place this really is!

Ashley Esuk (13)
Ormiston Park Academy, Aveley

162

Untitled

Warm and cosy as a freshly caught fire,
The cat comes and cuddles up beside me,
And I gradually fall into a deep, deep sleep.
It's like I'm the only person in the world,
I dream of things I wish I can be,
I dream of places I can go,
I dream of the world as it was my world.
Then morning comes to end,
As I always say to myself, 'I wish it was last night.'

Scarlet Anderson (13)
Ormiston Park Academy, Aveley

Spain

The sun is shining
The sea is blue
Spain, the place I like to go
To see parks
To see the shops
Spain is the place I will be
To be happy
To be free
Spain is the place I love to be.

Louis Chintua-Chigbu (12)
Ormiston Park Academy, Aveley

My Island Place

I know a place where it is out of this world.
I am happy because I like to see the blue sea.
The island is my favourite because it is blue sea.
I play with my friends on the beach
And then we go out for something to eat.
I like this place and I like the island
We make plans to meet again.

Soryia Khogiani (13)
Ormiston Park Academy, Aveley

163

My Dream Island

I know a place
Where I can relax
Beautiful sand
Giving me a tan

The weather is warm
The sand is hot
I've a tan
And my sister's not!

Honor Fry (13)
Ormiston Park Academy, Aveley

The Hungry Tiger

The sea is like a hungry tiger roaring in the wind
Splashing up the salty sea rocks
Eats anything he can find and see in its path
Just gnawing on his little snacks he has found
On quiet days April and November
The grass silently whistles in the wind
He plays in the water in the boiling hot weather
To cool himself down in the extreme weather conditions.

Jamie-Lee Carter (12)
Ormiston Park Academy, Aveley

Life

Life is like a leaf,
It comes in all shapes and sizes.
Some days everything is good and calm,
And the next everything is windy and rough.
Life is full of ups and downs,
That's just the way it goes.
But life goes on and we go off,
That's just the way the world goes around.

Lucy Jewell (12)
Ormiston Park Academy, Aveley

Poem Of What My Favourite Place Is

I wake up really excited that I'm going there
The lovely green grass
That brightens my day
I'm really excited on my way.
When I tee off with my dad who is the best
We'll beat the rest
When I get home from a long day
I have to wait for another day.

Mason Humphrey (12)
Ormiston Park Academy, Aveley

Beautiful Night

The whistling wind hitting the trees, like a bird gliding as free
The snow and the ice as white as a swan, it shines and sparkles all
night long
The dark night comes to a draw as the sun comes up,
Night is gone with no moon but just the sun
Everyone wakes and cheers the sun.

Jessica Twyman (11)
Ormiston Park Academy, Aveley

My Room

My room, a place of peace,
An area where I can be myself,
But in school I'm by myself where no one notices me,
This place is where I belong in my room
As I drag myself onto the school bus,
I know it's just another school day.

Sharon Sangotade (12)
Ormiston Park Academy, Aveley

165

My Lovely Dog Vader

In the day I play with my dog
She loves her food
I play with her, she plays with me and I play with her
My dog Vader barks a lot
Sometimes she's a pain but I love my dog Vader
She jumps on me.

Hayley Brown (11)
Ormiston Park Academy, Aveley

The Polar Bear

The polar bear waits for his prey,
every single night and day,
he waits for the seal in the icy breeze,
then he will catch it with one seize.
He dreams this dream every day,
he wants to live the polar bear way,
but he knows he can't because he's in a cage,
and inside he's bubbling with rage.
His roar rebounds off of the rusty metal bars,
he remembers his paradise,
but that paradise is long away now, so long, so far.
He remembers how grand he felt, so grand and so tall,
but here in the zoo he feels so very small.
He remembers the snowy blanket that covered his land,
But how that blanket differs to the metal upon which he stands.
The polar bear waits for his prey,
every single night and day,
he waits for the seal in the icy breeze,
then he will catch it with one seize.
He dreams this dream every day,
he wants to live the polar bear way,
but he knows he can't because he's in a cage,
and inside he's bubbling with rage.

Nick Parker (12)
Shenfield High School, Brentwood

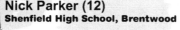

I'm Thinking . . .

I know what I'm thinking
I can see it all up here
Some of it is normal
And some a bit austere.

I think good and bad thoughts
Scary, happy and sad
When I let my thoughts out
Some people think I'm mad.

In there are laughing clowns
Ghosts and little men
Dragons, magic, mystery
Or maybe a dancing hen.

Some of my moving thoughts
Are really quite atrocious
But otherwise they're boring
Silent, still, motionless.

Sometimes I really wonder
What powers all those thoughts
There must be a supply
Otherwise there would be naught!

So where do they come from?
Who creates and puts them there?
Who rules over these little thugs
Tucked neatly under my hair?

I wish I knew the answers
To all these wondrous questions
It's really getting to me now
Like a disease or an infection.

Although I do know the answer
I don't need to shout or bawl
Cause of course it's my mind
So I'm ruler of it all!

Christian Haywood (12)
Shenfield High School, Brentwood

167

Everyone Together

Look all around you,
Humans everywhere,
None of them are perfect,
If they're here or there,
Wherever you may be,
China, Jamaica, oversea,
Even sitting in a tree,
Everybody is the same,
And that'll never change.

So you see,
That somehow you and me
Can change the world,
Stop wars,
Help the poor,
Because nobody's perfect,
Not even any leaders,
Chosen,
What for?

We can stop bullies,
And help goodies,
We can help the homeless,
And the boneless,
Altogether we can fight
For our rights,
And make the world
A better place.

Harrison Wood (11)
Shenfield High School, Brentwood

168

I Knew How To Be

From birth I knew what to be
I learned to walk
And became a tinker talk
The sassy smiles which slide on my face were joy
I was now a little boy
I knew how to be.

School was a trap I thought
A jail with old lady guards
But as the years went on
It was a match made in Heaven
To come out with a brain of the world
I knew how to be.

The eldest child I am
My brother and sister they sigh
With a laugh loved by lip
I cheer them up, we are a three!
I knew how to be.

The world is a maze
Full of problems, its beautiful birth
To lead us to dark deep death
Do you believe in God, afterlife?
Or myths and legends of power?
Or the thrill and joy of life?
The good and bad, brave and cowardice?
We all know how to be.

William Ryan (11)
Shenfield High School, Brentwood

My Poem

One day back in Aussie,
I was born, which sure is a worry,
I grew up with my mum and dad,
And a sister, who treated me very bad,
A dog which had a furry coat,
And my uncle, who owned a boat,
Then one night, when we were eating tea,
My dad told me something which took surprise to me.

He said that at the end of the year
We would move to the northern hemisphere,
To a place called the UK,
Meaning I wouldn't be an Aussie for another day.

But in exotic England, it isn't all bad,
Even though their accent can drive you mad,
And then there's the chittering wind,
Which sure takes away our lovely grin.

Last week I got a drum kit,
Now my mum wishes she never bought it!
Crash! Bang! Wallop! every single day,
I think my mum is moving to the USA!

Ben Oldham (12)
Shenfield High School, Brentwood

Who, What I Travel Unhindered

Who and what am I?
I am not dead or alive,
My body is gone,
But my soul still floats.

There's anger inside my dried fragile veins,
That once flowed with blood and love.
I still feel the pain and rage
As my whole world fades
Into the ashes of burning embers.

Not sure if I'm alive,
Not sure if I'm dead,
I'm not in Heaven,
Nor in Hell.
I am in a place in-between,
Where I can travel unhindered
But my feet have strings
Still attached to the living,
The life I once had, a life cut short.

No facts nor figures say that this sanctuary
I am now forced to call home
Is not real or non-existent,
But for me it's the closest I am going to get
To ever feeling the living.

It is a game that fate plays
A game of chase, but no one ever wins the race,
But it always makes sure you're well and safe.

Stephanie Nicholls (15)
Sir Charles Lucas Arts College, Colchester

The Alternative Sky

The sky is the floor on which God treads,
The stars are fallen glitter from a young child's art,
The clouds are the dust from a housewife's cleaning,
The birds are God's pets flown from their home.

The sun is a ripe orange freshly picked from
an ever-growing orchard,
The moon is our departed family members' ways
of lighting us in the dark,
We are different groups of creatures, intelligent and beautiful,
The sky's our imagination and the Earth is our mind.

Daniel Finch (13)
Sir Charles Lucas Arts College, Colchester

Big Ben

Oh Big Ben in all your glory,
but your cuts and bruises tell a different story.
Stationed there you've stood the test of time,
your bells keep you company while they sing and chime.
Men who had owned you had so much power,
while they praise you and seek to decorate your tower.
Speaking to us, smiling with your clock face,
your bells ring fast but maintain a pace.
They should be decorated with diamonds and jades,
not wood, but with liberty and justice you were made.
Against other monuments we take for granted,
like the Tower of Pisa which is really slanted.
The Statue of Liberty standing proud and tall,
safe in the knowledge that it will never fall.
The pyramids made out of sand and stone,
though in the wind they always groan.
For they are so always in demand,
you wonder, are they the greatest in the land?
For there is only one beauty that strikes ten,
our friend, Big Ben.

Timothy Huxham (12)
Sir Joseph Williamson's Mathematical School, Rochester

172

The Miserable Man

A man, a horrible man!
Who would eat whatever he can.
His brown body as brown as the colour
With one tooth like a knife
A miserable life.

Splash, splash in the mud
He fell over with a mighty thud
He was a penniless beggar
He lived in a pipe in tar
Right by a rusty car.

Eating roaches
Begging at all the passing coaches
Without a penny to his name
He hung his head in shame
And along came . . .

A man emerged from the smoke
He thought it was a joke
It said to get a great job
Then he glided away
Not listening to what he had to say

He got out of his tunnel
And blew through a funnel
It was a new day
He went away for a day, he didn't know what to say
And with a job waiting there he lay . . . happy!

Then there he was back on his feet
Walking to work in the sleet
He was waiting for a big boring treat
Working all day, hey!
He really wanted pay day!

Dominic Whittington (11)
Sir Joseph Williamson's Mathematical School, Rochester

Another One

As the coffin of the fallen soldier came in,
The sun began to dim,
And the choir sang a hymn.
A grieving widow mourned his death,
Remembering his last breath.

He was a valiant man,
Killed in his armoured van,
He could not have ran.
He was shot in the heart,
He lost a body part.

In the line of duty,
It was pure cruelty,
He should be remembered as royalty.
He gave all for Queen and country,
He was awarded for his gallantry.

As the coffin was laid to rest,
His mother thought of him as the best,
He fought in the east and west.
A soldier of Britain,
In history, his name will be written.

Idolise them,
Who are real men,
And especially him, Ben.
He did it all,
Big and small.

He fought for you,
And your family too,
Remember him, do.
He was killed in his armoured van,
He was a great man.

Amrik Bains (11)
Sir Joseph Williamson's Mathematical School, Rochester

The World Changes

The beautiful floating white ice,
Floating around the sea
Until the climate gets hotter
Polar bears try to survive
Because of the heat
They have nowhere to live
So polar bears start to die

When it all goes
You will know
That you will regret it

Why do it, why?
Ruin the wonderful ice
When it all goes
You will know
That you will regret it

So start now, go!
Save the living nature
Before it is gone!

As you will know
When it is gone
Because your house will be flooded

That is why you should
Stop your CO_2 waste
Save your energy
Do whatever you can
To save the long living nature

When it all goes wrong
You will know
That you will regret it.

Alexander Lai (12)
Sir Joseph Williamson's Mathematical School, Rochester

Slithery The Snake

A black adder goes past
One of the most venomous of all animals
Also the most deadly snake
Collecting its venom for some medicine samples
It's slithering
Quick move
Quickly hurry up and run
That snake is fast
Slow down now
It's stopped
Wait, it's on the move again
It's going to strike
Then give a nasty bite
Its teeth go under the skin
You can feel the sharpness of it
He pulls out his knife
And stabs the snake
He can see it is injured
And the man is badly wounded
The cut gets worse
Blood squirts out
It is as red as a berry
He lays on the green grass
The grass is long and spiky
The snake slithers to the bush beside him
The bush is scruffy
Just like his hair
It is short
But the snake is very long
And skinny.

Thomas Collins (11)
Sir Joseph Williamson's Mathematical School, Rochester

176

All About Me And My Family

My family lived in a house,
I had a pet mouse.
The name of this mouse was Bill,
He had a very strong will.
I love chocolate cake,
It is easy to bake.
My brother is weird,
He has a three-metre beard.
My mum is a leader,
She invented the E-reader.
Dad is a vet,
He helps a lot of pets.
My sister has three cats,
They are as mad as hats.
Our house is warmed by a fire,
But it is such a liar.
I hate oranges,
Nothing rhymes with them.
Roller coasters are fun,
Especially while eating a bun.
My favourite thing is school,
Closely followed by playing pool.
Animals are large and small,
Even when in the local mall.
My poem is ending,
It is a-bending.
It is weird and insane,
But not as dangerous as an upside-down plane.

Connor Williams (13)
Sir Joseph Williamson's Mathematical School, Rochester

Into The Forest

The forest looms into view,
through the dark, misty night.
As the moonlight steps into the forest,
the bird begins its flight.

It flies west,
into the gloom,
until a dark shape appears,
it will get there soon.

Into the forest,
the tired bird flies,
shrouded in darkness,
it drops from the skies.

Through the tangle of shrubs it goes,
on the brink of life and death.
It tries to lift its wings to fly,
as the branches and leaves are flashing by.

With a last ounce of strength,
it glides down to the ground.
But now it's in the forest,
neither lost or found.

Peter Selves (12)
Sir Joseph Williamson's Mathematical School, Rochester

Running - Haiku

Rabbit runs from fox,
Fox runs from the human kind;
We run from nothing.

Nicholas Wills (11)
Sir Joseph Williamson's Mathematical School, Rochester

178

Rugby

Some people say . . .
Rugby is such an aggressive game,
and winning is the only aim.
Dirty, muddy and unforgiving,
only the best continue living.
But it's such a great sport,
who'd of ever thought.
Dirty, soggy and very bruised up they'll get,
you'll like it, you'll love it, they'll hate it, I bet.
They're scared of our hooker, scared of our prop,
they'll tackle them and go crash, bang, wallop.
We ruck for the ball, we ruck for them all,
The line-out, the scrum, we'll show 'em how it's done.
We'll drive to the end, they'll need time to mend,
and when it's all over, they always ask . . .
Who was that team that beat us with a blast?

Jack Bryant (11)
Sir Joseph Williamson's Mathematical School, Rochester

The Four Elements: Earth, Fire, Wind And Water - Haiku

Earth is a planet
and it is also the ground
powerful and strong.

Fire is lava
like the ground it is strongest
when unexpected.

Wind is slow and long
never ending, helping us
but very deadly.

Water is liquid
different state than others
but twice as lethal.

Matthew Clarke (11)
Sir Joseph Williamson's Mathematical School, Rochester

179

The Real World

I start to walk in the morning,
I start to talk whilst walking.
We're walking, I'm walking.

The car pulls up close,
We step back,
From the car a man rose,
We start to feel nervous.
We're scared, I'm scared.

The man tries to grab us,
We make a run for school,
Running across the road in front of a school bus,
We see the school.
We're running, I'm running.

We run into the safety of the school and its huge gate,
Dodging between students.
Our hearts pumping at an unbelievable rate,
We get to class.
We're safe, I'm safe.

The day goes quickly,
Like someone's pressed fast forward,
We all move on swiftly,
At the end of the day we walk to the gates.
We're leaving, I'm leaving.

The man is there, outside the school,
He's a homeless tramp,
But definitely no fool,
We notice him.
We're nervous, I'm nervous.

We split up, my mate goes right,
And I go left,
My mate's the one the man wants to fight,
I sprint for home and help.
My mate's fighting, I'm sprinting.

180

I get home as help arrives for my mate,
I'm scared for him,
Only help will decide his fate.
I will try to get on with my normal life but
I'm shocked, I'm shocked.

Noah Hyde (11)
Sir Joseph Williamson's Mathematical School, Rochester

Old Building

Along the deserted road,
Stood a building all strong and bold.
The trees around it full of old leaves,
The man who owned the building was called Jeaves.
Jeaves was as rich as Bill Gates,
But still he had no mates.
The building protected by an electric fence,
Made this a worthy defence.
The building must have stood the test of time,
But what would make this moment special is if it was mine.

Stephen McSwiney (11)
Sir Joseph Williamson's Mathematical School, Rochester

In The Sky

Look at you flying ever so high,
Blending in with the colour of the sky.
Blue, purple, red and white,
From the yellow in the morning to the black at night.
Then I noticed something strange,
When you came over the mountain range,
Then realised you were a dragon,
And you sent me flying into a wagon.
I was badly injured as you see,
And really that was the end of me.

Griffin Huggett (12)
Sir Joseph Williamson's Mathematical School, Rochester

Homework - Haiku

Projects, books and thoughts
Pencils and dirty fingers
Stress, doubts, exhaustion.

James Wallace (11)
Sir Joseph Williamson's Mathematical School, Rochester

Nature, Wondrous Nature

I sometimes contemplate the wonders of nature,
wondrous nature.
Why do we have trees, or bees, or fleas?
Why is there sky, how are clouds so high?
I ponder, and wonder, and consider why,
Why is there wood?
Or wind, or water?
And why is there mud and is there a God?
Why is there nature, wondrous nature?
I ponder, and wonder, and consider why?
My, oh my, oh why?

Oliver Leonard (12)
Tendring Technology & Sixth Form College, Thorpe-le-Soken

My Brother!

My brother is cool,
I love him so much,
He's always there for me,
And this poem is what I think of him,
So let me try and make you see,
My brother is funny,
He loves his mummy,
He loves his father too;
Usually whatever you tell him, it's what he won't do!

Abigail King (11)
The Christian School, Takeley

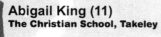

Some Things Just Have To Be Said

I apologise for these few broken letters,
Ask anyone else, and I'm certain they'd do better.
And maybe slushy poetry isn't your style,
But even if you laugh at me, at least I'll see you smile.

Now I know this isn't Shakespeare,
But it's all that I can do.
Metaphors just feel like chores,
And I want this to be true.

You're like that candle on the sea,
That floats on through the night,
And when you glow, all other things,
Are lost and out of sight.

You're not my second star in the sky,
You're better, you're the first.
You're like that longed for oasis,
That quenches all my thirst.

But like an oasis, when I draw closer,
You start to ripple away.
And when I try to talk to you,
I find no words to say.

They say I'm a hopeless romantic,
A novel without a word.
They say I am just a dreamer,
A song that's never heard.

I don't know how you do this to me,
My heart, it longs to fly.
Why do people always dream,
And yet are too scared to try?

So I'm going to say this to you,
And I want to say it true,
The truth is concealed in just five words,
I'm in love with you.

Rachael Chapman (13)
The Christian School, Takeley

183

Cheese Crackers

Cheese and crackers make a good pair
Banshees and dodos are quite rare
Dragons and fairies are such a myth
Fish and turkey make a good dish
Roses and dandelions are so pretty
Dragonflies and butterflies are so flitty
I like all things in nature and all food
I just don't like people being ever so rude.

Lara Hooke (11)
The Christian School, Takeley

Love Above!

Love above the world so sweet
Where everything's neat and complete
And it will be great and you'll never be late
Because God will be there and He will care
So believe in Him and Jesus too
And you'll get through to Heaven too.
(Thank you for reading, God bless you.)

Abigail Jackson (11)
The Christian School, Takeley

My Fantastic Holidays

Ibiza is amazing
Home to San Antonio and rave anthems
But there's so much more to see
Beautiful beaches and restaurants too
The atmosphere is oh so calm
The people are so friendly
The air is so warm and free of pollution
There's so much more than clubs
A great holiday destination for the whole family
Or just the teenagers themselves
There are so many different surrounding islands
It provides extra holidays in itself
It makes you feel so free and alive
So many beautiful things to see
The last bonus, you'll get a great tan
Another holiday that was a great experience
Was going to America
I met my grandad and cousins for the first time
I made friends I will never forget
The sights I saw were unforgettable
While I was there I travelled to Florida
And was fortunate enough to visit Disneyland
Never I thought I would ever do that
But oh so much it was worth it
The characters were so lifelike
It felt great to be a kid
I was so happy and smiled all day
What a treat for an 8-year-old
I have a brilliant mum to thank for that
I will remember both trips for eternity.

Shelmadine Andrews (13)
The Philip Morant School & College, Colchester

The Things Trees Hear

Trees hear many things
In summer, winter, autumn and spring
Some hear more than others
They listen to children and their mothers
They listen to the children play
As their leaves begin to fall and lay
When the morning gets nearer
And the forest gets clearer
The trees listen and hear
The crunching of their leaves
From the deer
They listen to the lumberjack
And his plans to cut
They hope for a longer life
And survive for another night
They listen to the families
Talk about their tragedies
When night is here
All is clear
For the owl to hunt tonight
Another day
For all to lay
And listen to the stream
When the leaves bustle
The trees all rustle
About the things they heard today
These
These are the things trees hear.

Ashleigh Hooper (12)
The Philip Morant School & College, Colchester

186

On The Train

As she sat on the train
She thought really hard
What route shall I take?
It kept going through her mind
Shall I carry on to the city,
Or shall I get off at the countryside?
What route shall I take?
It kept going through her mind
Shall I go to the busy city,
Or the quiet countryside?
What route shall I take?
It kept going through her mind
Shall I go to the shops,
Or shall I go to see the animals?
What route shall I take?
It kept going through her mind
Shall I go to see the famous buildings,
Or shall I go to the pretty fields?
What route shall I take?
It kept going through her mind
The train came to a halt
She looked out the window to the countryside
Shall I get off?
It was going through her mind.

Anna Davies (12)
The Philip Morant School & College, Colchester

A Diary For A Sad One

Christmas passes and I have sent my Christmas present to him
I wonder when it will get there, I wait on a whim
I pass the days wondering will he ever come?
I admire my mother for being as strong as a bone
My heart fills with sadness when I realise I can't
I think of him, I think, I shan't, I shan't, I shan't
But all I can think of is his face
I pull my own hair when I think of his funeral case
Sometimes in my dreams I hear
The screams, the yells as if it was someone near
In the day I feel anger weighing down
I wonder if it really is me, or if it's just science
I occasionally laugh or just weakly smile
I feel like an outcast, an exile
As my heart melts away while I wait in darkness
It screws up in tightness
You will always be my
Partner
Brother
Acquaintance
Friend
Family
Best friend.

Emily Smakowski (12)
The Philip Morant School & College, Colchester

188

What Happens When It Snows?

There's lots of snow,
A lot to throw,
A snowman bigger than a man.

The children sledge
Down into the hedge.

Snowball fights
Give real frights
To the old
Who hate the cold.

Outside there is a snowman
Holding a Coca Cola can.

So there's lots of snow,
Lots to throw,
And children sledge
Into a hedge.

And that's what happens in the snow!

Joseph Lawton (13)
The Philip Morant School & College, Colchester

People

There was a boy called
Jim who lived in a bin
Harry who was friends with Larry
Sam who liked ham
Jack who has an Apple Mac
Sam who ate jam

There was a girl called
Kyla who liked to 'smila'
Brooke who lived by the book

There was a teacher called Mr Emms
He was great, everyone wanted to be his friend.

Gareth Hughes (12)
The Philip Morant School & College, Colchester

189

The Voices In My Head

The little voices in my head
tell me they know best,
they follow me where I go,
before I even know.

They always say we're a team,
but they can be so mean,
they are always in my head,
even when I'm in bed.

I wonder if they will go away,
haunt someone else someday?
Sometimes I just want to disappear and run,
but I know that won't be any fun.

But however today they are gone,
I hate feeling so alone,
I just don't know what to say,
I'm feeling so lost today.

Amy Neill (12)
The Philip Morant School & College, Colchester

Blanket From Heaven

A soft white blanket
So fluffy and light
That's just landed in the night

Magically glistening is the ice
As everyone's wishing they don't slide
And the people who don't have so much pride

The blanket dropped all over the trees
To make the ugliest of all as pretty as they can be
This beautiful blanket is so thick I almost can't see

Finally it will drift away
And there won't be any by the bay
The soft white blanket goes away.

Ella Myall (12)
The Philip Morant School & College, Colchester

Snowday

Snow is soft, just like a feather
The snow is fun but not the weather

It's fun to go down riding a sledge
Until you fall and land in a hedge

Snow is fun to throw at men
We go out and play till half-past ten

It's fun to shove people in the snow
Until you go home with a freezing toe

Snow is always fun to play in
And hope you don't trip and fall in a bin.

Nick Rippingale (13)
The Philip Morant School & College, Colchester

Just Another Day

Bleep, bleep, bleep, bleep,
The alarm sounds shrill and severe,
'OK, OK,' I groan, 'I'm here, I'm here!'
Rolling over it's time to emerge
From my cosy bed,
Where I was on the verge
Of a great dream.
A warrior bold,
Fighting with honour, it was about to unfold.
However, it was not to be,
Into the shower I had to flee.
Thirty minutes and I was in the car,
Five miles to school, so it is not too far.
Through the school gates and ever nearer,
To eight whole hours,
Oh dear! Oh dear!
Maths, English, break and more,
Science, lunch then . . . F&T,
Oh what a bore!

Charlie Woodman (13)
Thorpe Hall School, Southend-on-Sea

191

1666

Stepping out the door
Onto the streets
Death was all you saw
And life was all you seek.

See the infected, see the dead
See them slowly bleed to death.

Roaming around
To look for more,
But every town
Has the Devil's hor'r.

The curse has spread, and more were killed
Terror struck and fear caved in.

Coughs and colds
Did not compare
When punishment from God
Filled the air.

Families destroyed, friends were lost
In this darkened time of loss.

The Devil appeared
In every face
His evil spread
Around the place.

A time of chaos, a time of despair
A single candle with a burning flare.

Hell struck out
As flames grew high
Into the midnight
Darkened sky.

Satan reached, with fiery hands
His fingertips touched a darkened land.

There were screams
There were yells
There was burning
And there was Hell.

Olivia Conway (12)
Thorpe Hall School, Southend-on-Sea

Nobody's Home

The little cat cried at the door,
Nobody loves him anymore,
It seems his owner's gone away,
Not for a week, not for a day.

She's moved on to another street,
Left poor Archie with nothing to eat,
No more love and no more care,
An empty house with no one there.

When dark falls the sun goes down,
Poor little Archie wanders around,
Scary noises, darkened places,
No more kind, familiar faces.

As he lays beneath a tree,
Remembering how it used to be,
Very wary, so unsure,
He runs quickly to the old back door.

The light goes on, someone's home,
At least he isn't all alone,
The door opens wide, in he goes,
And snuggles up to a lady's toes.

A new owner moved in today,
She tells him it will be okay,
He looks around, it's much the same,
He settles down, he's home again.

Charlotte Brake (12)
Thorpe Hall School, Southend-on-Sea

193

The Runaway Slave

With the clang of the chains and bang of a hammer
The shackles are broke,
With a sweaty face and clothes which are soaked,
He won't be found; he can't be saved,
This is the curse of the runaway slave.

The slap of feet hitting the ground,
The smashed open gate with a shattering sound.
He won't be found; he can't be saved,
This is the curse of the runaway slave.

A scared, muddled brain, which is turning insane,
He turns round the corner of the little old lane.
He won't be found; he can't be saved,
This is the curse of the runaway slave.

He sprints across the park without being seen,
Crawling in the field, his legs turning green.
He won't be found, he can't be saved,
This is the curse of the runaway slave.

He climbs over fences as fast a bee,
Without a scratch or a graze to his knee.
He won't be found; he can't be saved,
This is the curse of the runaway slave.

The bitter smell of rusted metal,
And the horrible sound of a screaming kettle.
He won't he found; he can't he saved,
This is the curse of the runaway slave.

With the howl of the wind calling his name,
He fears it's his mind playing a game.
He won't be found; he can't be saved,
This is the curse of the runaway slave.

Callum Watt (13)
Thorpe Hall School, Southend-on-Sea

The World Is Everything

The world of the worlds
Is everything
I am the world
The world of everything.

You have it
You feel it
It gets so powerful
The bad is coming.

You notice all around you
The bad is coming
It gets so powerful
You can't take it.

After a while you notice
It gets worse and worse and worse
It's not just strange thinking it's true
The bad is coming.

You're so worried, so scared
You think, tell someone, tell someone
You tell someone
It's worse, the bad gets close.

The world of the worlds
Is everything
I am the world
The world of everything.

Then the bad is here
Coming and coming and coming
The end is here
The end, the end
The bad is here.

Jonathan Perkins (12)
Thorpe Hall School, Southend-on-Sea

195

The Dream

Cupid gave her the dart,
But he broke her heart,
She jumped into the sky,
As the night was approaching by,
Fooled by love,
She asked herself if there is any white dove,
Love is unjust, love is unfair.

On the dark stormy waters she was pale,
As the wind whipped around her in the gusty gale,
The white horses were galloping,
As her sprint was travelling,
What caused her pain?
Him, he said she was too poor,
So he went off to marry another squaw,
Love is unjust, love is unfair.

Her eyes went into a dead stare,
She remembered all those things he said to her,
All she could taste was salt, words were slurred,
And with her dying breath she said love may be unjust and unfair,
But it is also something that people can bear,
Her life was slipping away,
She was now at the bottom of the bay,
She closed her eyes.

Next morning she woke up to a big surprise,
The horrible scene,
Had only been a dream,
She went to work and then she saw him,
The man from her dream,
The reason that she jumped and screamed,
And she whispered to herself, love is unjust, love is unfair.

Annabel Streeton (12)
Thorpe Hall School, Southend-on-Sea

196

Run Away

My fear rose as I
Was a fox being chased by hounds
Running
 Running
  Running
   So fast

The pain, so much pain
The stabbing, pain in my back
I want to stop but if I do they will get me
Running
 Running
  Running
   So fast

Leaves brush past my face
Stones hurt my feet
As I run on them
Blood and cuts cover my feet
I need to stop but I can't
Running
 Running
  Running
   So fast

My owner is chasing me
If I stop he will kill me
I am not meant to run away
Running
 Running
  Running
   So fast.

Rowena White (12)
Thorpe Hall School, Southend-on-Sea

197

Death Of A Whale

My species is endangered,
Soon we'll be gone,
If the torture of whales
Is allowed to go on.

I'm one of the smallest in my family,
That doesn't stop Japanese men hunting me,
I'm fast and I'm playful, I wish that they knew,
How much that they hurt me by all that they do.

I'm 32 foot and weigh nearly 5 tons,
I'm heavy I know, but my life's almost done,
So for now I'll enjoy it as I glide through the water,
That's what my mum said but they've already caught her.

I'm close to the edge of the polar ice pack,
I'm going so fast, then feel pain on my back,
They've shot me, there's blood, I'm dragged on the rope,
My breath's nearly gone, I'm beginning to choke.

Their faces flash past,
There's now no debating,
It's wicked just what these men are creating.

How cruel and unkind the death of a whale,
No more remarkable song it's a screaming death howl,
This is what they've done to me.

Lewis Brake (14)
Thorpe Hall School, Southend-on-Sea

198

Menacing Moon

Dark clouds cover over the hills
While looking your mind is sent into chills
The moon eventually it starts to rise
The tiny bird no longer flies
The town no longer able to see
Not even the tiny little flea
While the fires go out
No sound, no whisper, not even a shout
Stars brighten stayed in their place
The sky looking like a colour base
No travellers come
The cold whistles and your hands become numb
The lake looking as blue as normal
However not looking as close it is abnormal
You can see the reflection of the sky
While watching, the sun comes up and the moon dies
Wait the sun is here too, quick
The clock, not knowing, had been going tick, tick, tick
The sun is revealed as it sets
However do not fret
There is another night
The sun is golden wondrous sight.

Louise Banks (12)
Thorpe Hall School, Southend-on-Sea

Break Time

Frantic, rushing to get the ball,
Quick, it's break time, out of school!
On the concrete or on the field,
Hope the opposition yield!

Up and down, left and right,
Scaring the defenders with our might,
Oh look, a tackle to the left of me,
And I fall down in agony!

Connor Smith (13)
Thorpe Hall School, Southend-on-Sea

199

Space

As I lay back in my bed
I have all these thoughts going on in my head
What's it like looking from space?
Is the Earth just a tiny place?

I think of the rockets shooting up in the air,
What would it be like if I was there?
Would I see the stars oh so bright?
Would I see shooting stars brightening up the night?

What if I landed on the moon?
Would it take a long time to get there? Would it be soon?
Would I see aliens? Oh I hope so,
But then the night would be over, then I'd have to go.

Back in bed I've decided what I need to get,
A telescope, then I'd see the stars I bet,
Then I can pretend that I'm really up in space,
Looking down on the Earth as just a tiny place.

Jessica Rimington-Cross (12)
Thorpe Hall School, Southend-on-Sea

Happy Times

Waking to the smell of pancakes, heart racing,
jumping down the stairs.
Surprise! Mum and Dad bring forth a brand new bike!
Shocker, a real shocker!

Bright, illuminous and soft, as the wheels spin the air brushing
across my hair.
I hear children closing on me,
They trip my bike over, *boom!*
I hit the crumbly rock hard floor.
In pain, trying to gain consciousness as the kids laugh at me,
Embarrassed, red-hot,
I fall, fall, fall . . .

Matthew Law (12)
Thorpe Hall School, Southend-on-Sea

200

Friends Should Be Forever

A friendship is definitely meant to last,
Not something that should end fast,
Me for you and you for me,
Having a friend makes me so happy,
We are together through bad and good,
Like the best of friends should.

I am you and you are me,
Like the rain is the sea,
We confide in each other,
Never dare to tell another,
Everything is discussed,
Secrets are definitely a must.

When you are low and feel down,
Never put on a frown,
Anything that is said,
I'll stand by you 'cause you're my best friend.

Alice Diaper (12)
Thorpe Hall School, Southend-on-Sea

Shipped Away

Clank and a bang of shackles thousands locked up, the smell
of white hatred in the air - shipped away
They limboed on the slave ship, shipped away to the middle
of the ocean
The sight of white waves and overboard slaves - shipped away
Hundreds of dead around us, the sharks surrounding us -shipped
away
Inside the boat, trapped under the deck - shipped away
Dead bodies, bad smells like rotten sewage and lots of rats -
shipped away
The shouts of the captain telling us, the taste of bitter hatred -
shipped away.

Monté Hodges (13)
Thorpe Hall School, Southend-on-Sea

201

Deep Dark Deck

Lying down strapped in chains
Living through Hell, heaving
Limbo
Trying to survive
Struggling, struggling to communicate.

Under the dark deck
All that surrounds me
Water, corpses moaning
Limbo
Blocking out noises
Struggling, struggling to live

Sunlight peaking
Through the upper
Deck
Dying slowly
Limbo.

Washington Ali (12)
Thorpe Hall School, Southend-on-Sea

The Wave

Big hard wave all surrounding me,
Hitting me, waking me, hurting me,
And all surrounding me.
You hear the scream,
You touch the scream,
You feel the scream,
But yet it won't stop.
Hit, smash, whip,
All shivering me,
Deep, deep down,
In the dark surrounding me,
But yet it still won't stop.

Kieran Groves (12)
Thorpe Hall School, Southend-on-Sea

202

Darkness . . .

Hot, flustered, sweaty, tired
Trapped, nowhere to go
Strapped down like a lion in a circus cage.

The smell
Oh my Lord
It smelt of rotted corpse, decaying fish heads, stale blood
And gangrenous pus.

The horror of glowing eyes looking at me
Dead people lying beside me
A woman pregnant
Begging for her life helplessly.

I see hope,
An island awaiting me
I stand on hard ground
And run, run, run, quicker and quicker . . .

Joseph Chappell (13)
Thorpe Hall School, Southend-on-Sea

Going To School

I go to school each day,
I sometimes lose my way;
Every day it goes through my head,
I could go back home to bed.
I could play on Xbox, COD's calling me,
Or make myself some toast and tea . . .
But somehow I find myself at the gate,
I can't even be late.
It could be worse, I won't go insane,
Only seven hours till I go home again.

Alex Horn (13)
Thorpe Hall School, Southend-on-Sea

203

Why Is The Winter So Long?

In the summertime we endure the heat,
then in the winter we must cover our feet,
why are the winters so long?

From winter to spring we hear birds sing,
yet from autumn to winter,
not even the snap of a splinter,
why are the winters so long?

Winter seems so long,
yet summer so short,
shouldn't it be even?
That's what I thought.

So when we're at the end of winter,
hearts racing as fast as a sprinter,
winter is finally over!
Why was that winter so long?

Harvey Richardson-Shii (12)
Thorpe Hall School, Southend-on-Sea

The Non-Poem

I was asked to write a poem,
I didn't know where to start.
I wanted to write something meaningful,
Something from the heart.
I thought of themes and rhyming words,
Of similes and things.
But the more I tried, the harder it got,
Oh, where should I begin?

Keir Coford (13)
Thorpe Hall School, Southend-on-Sea

204

The Capture Of Misfortune

I went out hunting for some food,
I had my spear to kill the animal.
I was crawling as secretly as a lion,
And about to pounce at the creature,
I jumped, I stopped in midair,
Looking up; a white man handcuffed me.

I turned my head, there were many from different tribes,
Thousands at this camp,
Every one of them black.
There was a ship as tall as our Mount Kilimanjaro,
I was dreading the worst.
Handcuffed to as wooden bed,
The question racing through my mind, eating at my soul was . . .
Where am I going?
This really was the capture of misfortune.

Calum Neale (12)
Thorpe Hall School, Southend-on-Sea

Death

The elevator doors opened,
There he was, lying
Like an empty body, no one inside.
All wired up, with me not knowing if his eyes will ever open.
Nurses around him in white cloaks, like angels.

Suddenly the heart monitor started bleeping
Like an ambulance was cutting through the room.
My heart started punching against my stomach -
blub, blub, blub
Getting louder, screaming, howling,
Nurses ran in, electrocuting his body with shockers,
I had to leave, I could not watch this.
One hour later in I go, the nurses whisper in my ear,
'I'm sorry he's gone . . . '
My whole world fell apart.

Joseph Neidus (12)
Thorpe Hall School, Southend-on-Sea

205

The Scream

Can you see me on the bridge?
I'm stepping closer to the edge,
My head held in my hands,
I let out a scream.
Can you see me? Is it a dream?
You may think I'm scary,
I may fill you with fear,
Some say I bring them close to tears.
Can you see me? How do I make you feel?
Am I just a picture? Or am I real?
For I have come from somewhere,
Maybe inside someone's head.
Can you see me? Do I fill you with dread?
Or do I just make you laugh
Or maybe smile?
Do you find yourself looking at me for a little while?
Do I transfix you?
Can you tear yourself away from me?
Will you visit me tomorrow?
We'll have to wait and see.
I'm forever stuck in time,
You may think that's mean,
You can see me when you want to.
For I'm simply just a scream.

Katy Conybear (11)
Townley Grammar School for Girls, Bexleyheath

206

The Mona Lisa

Behind her beautiful eyes
Are where the mystery lies
Imagine if she can speak?
Will she be unique?

Her amazing smile that shines
So brightly as if to say a sign
Her wiseness makes people stare
Her wiseness is shown by her long black hair

We look and study her for quite a while
Who was she? Where did she come from?
Why is she showing her beautiful smile?

Her face, a beauty is what we see
I hope you would agree with me
Her smile is pure and full of hope
But how would she have really coped?

Her dress is made of rich silk
That is dark green and red
As she poses in a straight position
Like a piece of thread

Behind her beautiful eyes
Is this where the mystery lies?

Bunmi Adeoye (11)
Townley Grammar School for Girls, Bexleyheath

Café Terrace At Night

The moonlight dripped from the sky in patches
Staining the streets below
The jewels in the sky competing for attention
Appeared in their thousands to make a night
So bright to lodge themselves in the hearts
Of those underneath

The people in the street stopped suddenly
Half aware of the silver filtering into their hearts
While the multitudes in the café froze as one
And, sheltered from the liquid sun, strained
Unaware of their longing for a glimpse of the feeling
They saw on the street

The eyes in the building
Could but watch in breathless anticipation
As the moonlight seemed to blossom
Flourishing, pushing back the wilting café light
Until something snapped it
And Paris breathed once more

And no one but the furtive artist in the shadows
Captured the moment on canvas.

Sammy Baptiste (15)
Townley Grammar School for Girls, Bexleyheath

Tremor

What tremor does shelling bring?
The shrill of wails that linger in the air
Trenches so dark and deep
No prayers, no bells
No tenderness of patient minds
Just me, myself and I.

In the magnitude of silence
Hope emerges
In the eeriness that is known, it envelopes
Closer and closer
Drowning the silence as it approaches
While you cower down in vain.

Will your screams of horror evaporate?
Will they yield dividends?
Will the hope that you feel conquer the pain?
Will you see the unnatural humps that surround you?
Will you recognize the doom of your youth?
Will you think of those who see it too?

Omolefe Ohioma (13)
Townley Grammar School for Girls, Bexleyheath

Bikini

Not only pool and sea,
But horizon as well.
Ripples cover LA,
Spring to the sky, you're free.
Responsibility?
No more reality,
I've escaped to LA.
Roll the shutters down, closed.
Collapse on a chair and lay.
Let the heat seduce you.
Let the flames add colour.
Exhale fresh air and sweat.
She'd choose a bikini.
Hot tiles, scaled by bare feet,
Make it hotter, hotter!
I'm in LA England!

Jasmine Robinson (15)
Townley Grammar School for Girls, Bexleyheath

Dancing Flames

He danced in my room,
And he danced on the beach,
I saw my lover in the flames,
Burning, burning is all I see.

He beckons me into his fiery realm,
His hand outstretched,
The flames burning my eyes,
I cannot hold tears back.

I saw a waltz in my room,
I saw a foxtrot on the beach,
I saw my lover in the flames,
Burning, burning is all he says.

He dances in the street,
He dances in the sea,
I see my lover in the sky,
Light, light now I see.

I go to the water's edge,
My hand outstretched,
He leaves my cold hand,
I must not hold him back.

Anna Kamdar (12)
Westcliff High School for Girls, Westcliff-on-Sea

Lust, Love, Loss

When men finish relationships they don't cry
Barely let out a tut or a sigh,
But is it best to keep the feelings inside
Have no one in which to confide?
When women finish relationships there is a wave of emotion
They surround themselves with excessive commotion,
Let it out, let it out
Exhaust from all they shout.
One is from Venus, one from Mars
Both shine like a pearl amongst the stars,
Perhaps there is more in common than we think
Maybe if we stopped and stared, even just a blink.
Like a virgin losing a child
Our loneliness is wild,
We can try to cure this with coffee and cream
In vain hope to cement our dream.
So let the raindrops fall down tonight
Cleanse our fears all through the night,
Let the thunder bellow
Soothing like the cello.
The car exhaust, the cement haze
Leaving us in a loveless daze,
One may cross their heart and hope to die
Knowing it's their own cheating heart that made them cry.
Thinking they were your hero
Reality knows they were a clueless zero,
Fact and fiction blurs
Knowing your heart is still hers.
On the crest of the wave
Is where you felt most brave,
Thinking you had a pearl
Not just a little girl.
Even if it is your friends that surround you
Their lack of interest won't pull you through,
So often falling flat on your face
You hate to see yourself as a disgrace
If you catch a glimpse of the cream white of her eyes
Move down to the voluptuous thighs,

The lust still present
But you are hesitant.
Thinking you couldn't stand her but you really can't stand yourself
Is perhaps the biggest threat to your health,
Knowing you could end it all
But still you stall.
They say love is blind but it is also deaf
Because lovers cannot hear until nothing is left,
Till an end fit for the start
Till all the love has been torn apart.

Matthew Diamond (17)
West Kent College, Tonbridge

213

The Clouds Of A Soul
(In the style of Anne Bronte - 'Gloomily the Clouds')

Violent waves crashing,
On goes the raging night,
Save me
From the thunder and lightning
That clouds my judgment,
The pounding of my stormy brain
Beating to my raining heart,
Tearing through the last remains,
Outdone, at last!

The rush of winds
So strong,
To tip the balance
Shattering the fog that surrounds me,
Uttering the flooding secrets
That fall from their hailing lips,
As hot tears stream from their ghostly eyes,
Watching gloomily as the clouds pass by.

The vortex of screams that
Sear into the sky
Save me
From he treacherous rain
Of my overcast soul,
Misguided and led
Into the storm that brews above,
No, in my head,
I cannot be saved from myself.

Shanisa Emmons (18)
West Kent College, Tonbridge

214

Little Red Riding Hood

Skipping along in the lonely wood,
A little girl pulled back her hood,
Little Red Riding Hood held her basket,
And something more precious in a casket,
And at the front of Grandma's house,
Was a wolf with a stomach the size of a mouse,
'I'm so hungry!' he cried,
Then opened the door to look inside,
An old grandma sitting down,
Her eyes were blue and her hair was brown,
The wolf thought, yum!
And down she went into his tum,
'That wasn't enough,' the wolf said,
He put Grandma's clothes on and went to bed,
The wolf waited a long time,
He looked at the clock, half-past nine,
The wolf got up on the floor,
And went downstairs to open the door,
Not the front door but the fridge door,
And then he saw,
A world of food in every drawer,
Food here,
Food there,
It was food heaven everywhere,
He filled his face with cake and nosh,
Not thinking of the bill and dosh,
On a full belly,
He felt like jelly,
Then went to bed,
Without watching the telly,
When he woke he saw a girl,
But he had a hangover and wanted to hurl,
The girl pulled back her hood and dropped the basket,
Then she opened the very special casket.
Out came a gun,
And then, bang, bang, bang,
She shot a dart used to stun,
The wolf went crashing to the floor,

215

Then the wolf woke up once more,
To find himself over a fire,
With his hands and feet tied up with wire,
'You ate my granny,
So I'll eat you,
I've always wanted to taste wolf stew!'

Jonathan Camilleri (12)
Wilmington Grammar School for Boys, Wilmington

If I Had A Time Machine

If there was a time machine,
it would fulfil a lifelong dream.
I'd visit the present, future and the past,
I'd see the day that would be my last.
At the click of a button I would disappear,
a different place, another year.
The skies blue, grass still green,
things the future has never seen.
Flying vehicles placed on clouds,
scientists would have been so proud.
A better life with better things,
whoever imagined cars with wings?
My time machine is another chance,
to seize a memory a second glance.
Another victory in most people's eyes,
a cause of change in those lives.
It's amazing what the touch of a button can do,
sending you to things untrue.
A square box of magic placed on the floor,
quickly knocks upon time's door.
Perfect patients, a button to press,
a whirling circle of dates, what a mess!
Your journey begins;
it is out of sight,
until you see that blazing light.

Lauren Russell (15)
Woodlands School, Basildon

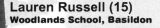

216

If I Had A Time Machine

If I had a time machine,
All chrome, amazing but small,
I wouldn't travel the galaxy,
I couldn't visit them all,
I wouldn't rescue the dinosaurs,
All so big and tall,
I'd leave it all the same way you see,
I wouldn't change the world,
I'd sit in a chair all day,
Thinking how to find a way,
To bring back all the ones you loved,
Taken from you without a nudge,
I wouldn't save the world,
Come back as a hero,
I wouldn't visit Egypt,
And take over as pharaoh,
I wouldn't steal a star for love,
Or fly to you like a dove,
I wouldn't take my family,
I wouldn't take my friends,
I would keep it all to myself,
Until the very end.

Jessica Hardy (14)
Woodlands School, Basildon

If I Had A Time Machine

There it is shining in the sun,
Waiting, silent, mysterious.
Silently it beckons me closer,
And I cannot refuse the call.

Many times I have travelled,
Through decades, time and space,
In my own mystical machine,
Investigating things that passed.

So I open the glistening red door,
Anxious and unaware,
Of the adventures that shall await me,
Wherever I may arrive.

I reach under the seat,
I press the button,
I guide the gear stick to seventh gear,
And I am gone.

There is a jolt as I land,
Steam clears from the windows,
And I am parked on a narrow street,
Surrounded by record hops and ice cream shops.

I glance at the date on the radio,
The year nineteen fifty-six,
I step out of the car,
Like an alien on foreign ground.

A few strange stares from people around,
As I wander into the nearest diner,
Elvis Presley plays on the juke box,
Teenagers dancing at the bar.

Girls wearing neck scarves,
Boys in leather jackets,
Just how my mother has described,
'So this is the fifties.'

Rosie Gulliver (14)
Woodlands School, Basildon

218

If I Had A Time Machine

If I had a time machine,
I'm not sure how I'd feel.
No one's ever had a time machine,
Would I be the first one?

I'm not sure.

Mine would look just like a clock,
Only it'd be man-sized.
It'd be orange like my beside clock,
It'd have a door just at the side.

Oval-shaped.

Inside the clock would be simple,
Not too many buttons, just three big ones.
The instructions also simple;
Red for stop, green for go and blue for a toilet break.

Just in case.

Using my time machine I'd travel,
Go to the past, undo my wrongs.
With this machine I'd use to travel,
I'd change other lives for the better.

They need it.

All I'd have to do is move the hands,
Anti-clockwise to visit the past.
Back one year with every tock of the hands,
I could even go back to the day I was born.

Was I cute?

With my time machine I'd be free,
I'd visit the past, everyone's past.
Back to the time when we were free,
If only I had a time machine.

I hope some day I'll have a time machine.

Leslie Yonta (14)
Woodlands School, Basildon

219

If I Had A Time Machine

If I had a time machine I would go to Devon
Show cavemen the invention of the refillable gas lighter
Go back to Germany in 1940
To tell Hitler to shave his moustache
Go back two thousand years
And tell Mary and Joseph that there really was room in the inn
Pop back to 1994
Tell my mum to call me Ben Dover
Travel back to the pyramids of Egypt
And write, 'The almighty Rob Lawler was here. PS: Gordon Brown is
an idiot'
Just 'cause I could
Maybe I would visit the founder of McDonald's
Just so I could show him fat-free burgers with Weight Watchers
I would tell The Beatles that they were actually bigger than Jesus!
Or maybe, just maybe
I would destroy the time machine there and then
After all if I changed the past
Maybe there may not be a future
The world seems OK the way it is
And as my old mum always say
Why fix something that isn't broken?

Robert Lawler (15)
Woodlands School, Basildon

220

If I Had A Time Machine

Fiery galvanized iron glimmering with fine delight,
As the echoing machine signals a location in the sight,
Past, present, future locked into one,
Travelling far beyond creation of the sun.

Discovering an unsolved mystery,
Experiencing all the history,
The iron machine the size of a whale,
Rocket-shaped engine ready to sail.

Visiting my future generation,
It would be a great sensation,
Knowing the beginning time,
Searching for the valuable dime.

The time machine would teach me everything,
And I would not need anything,
Amazing facts I always wanted to know,
3000BC would be the time I would go.

Wandering around the depth of the Earth,
Witnessing the universe's birth,
If only I had . . .
If only I had a time machine.

Ying Sung (15)
Woodlands School, Basildon

If I Had A Time Machine

If I had a time machine,
It would be in the shape of a cloud.
So bold, so bright, so colourful,
Oh I would be so proud.

My device, oh it could glide,
Over ground, seas, through skies.
First time I flew my time machine,
I had to close my eyes.

The view from above was breathtaking,
I could see everyone in my town.
Their happy faces full of glee,
I knew I would never feel down.

And no one could resist,
To come and take a ride.
A ride with me and Bunny Bear,
Her eyes I'd have to hide.

But I'd only take my closest friends,
They'd all be VIP.
So no one else could tag along,
Except of course for me.

Eleanor Dunne (14)
Woodlands School, Basildon

If I Had A Time Machine

If I had a time machine,
I would travel the universe.
Back and forth I would go,
But never now.

I would stop and stare at dinosaurs,
Watching them charge around.
I would watch the future,
Transform before my eyes.

All from my little cylinder box,
The time machine.
With the thousands of buttons inside,
Just waiting to be pushed.

So I do,
A different year every day.
Another place to go,
And another adventure.

I whizz around in my box,
And never want to stop.
I'd love a time machine,
I'd never be bored again.

Charlotte Clift (14)
Woodlands School, Basildon

If I Had A Time Machine

As a thought popped in my brain,
I thought of all that wretched pain,
If I could change it back then,
I would have saved so many men,
And stopped all that poor blood shed.

A million years ago,
Watch all those dinosaurs grow,
Having fights and only one friend,
Then to suddenly have it all end,
Watched all that poor blood shed.

See my family, the old and new,
All the struggles we've gotten through,
All the memories that would fade,
And all the memories that will be made,
If I had a time machine.

If I had a time machine,
I wouldn't have the same routine,
I would have variety,
I'd be different from society,
If I had a time machine.

Jack Francis (14)
Woodlands School, Basildon

If I Had A Time Machine

If I had a time machine I'd whizz through time and space,
I'd bring laughter to the world and I'd put a smile on every face.
I'd go into the future; I'd go back to the past,
I'll travel about so stealthily, so quietly and so fast.
I'd go into the future and solve the unexplained,
I'd go into the past and be the first to invent a train.
I'd stop global warming,
And prevent people from yawning.
I'd put air fresheners into the sewer networks,
And design a new range of skirts.
I'd create a new planet for snails,
Next door would live all of the whales.
I'd need to visit them regularly,
As sometimes they can get a bit hairy.
There would be marmalade skies,
And people would have magic eight ball eyes.
The world would be my snow globe,
I'd lace it with a red, velvet robe.
I'd cherish it with all my love,
I'd keep it warm with a wooly glove.

Emily Pumfrett (14)
Woodlands School, Basildon

Ballet Point Shoes

The soft silky touch of the satin point shoes,
With tears and scuffs which give the clues,
Class after class their pitter, patter surrounds,
Caressing my ankles the velvet ribbons twist around.

Their pink, shiny, glossy, glimmers in the light,
A star-like grace they hold tonight,
Their comfort soft as the touch of a feather,
I shall hold them close forever and ever.

With a glance they'll seem just points to you,
Just a tatty excuse of ballet point shoes,
But look deep within and you will see,
That these shoes truly are a part of me.

Izabel Oliver (12)
Woodlands School, Basildon

226

Young Writers Information

We hope you have enjoyed reading this book - and that you will continue to enjoy it in the coming years.

If you like reading and writing poetry drop us a line, or give us a call, and we'll send you a free information pack.

Alternatively if you would like to order further copies of this book or any of our other titles, then please give us a call or log onto our website at www.youngwriters.co.uk.

Young Writers Information
Remus House
Coltsfoot Drive
Peterborough
PE2 9JX
(01733) 890066